CONTENTS

D1400428

Installation Instructions for e-Medsys® Educational Edition 125

ABOUT e-Medsys®

The e-Medsys® Solution Suite from TriMed Technologies is a fully integrated and fully online practice management (PM) system, electronic health records (EHR) system, and patient portal used across the country in thousands of medical offices. The e-Medsys® EHR is 2008 CCHIT-certified in Ambulatory Medicine, Cardiovascular Medicine, and Child Health. For more information about TriMed Technologies, visit www.trimedtech.com.

The e-Medsys® Educational Edition from TriMed Technologies is a custom version of this powerful product. Since e-Medsys® is completely online, it is completely portable, allowing you to work on your exercises on any computer that has e-Medsys® installed—both in the computer lab and at home—without losing any work.

e-Medsys® Educational Edition has two interfaces—a practice management (PM) interface, and an electronic health records (EHR) interface. These two interfaces work seamlessly together, forming a practical and powerful total practice management system (TPMS)—allowing all tasks in a medical office to be performed electronically. The EHR interface is accessed through a menu drop-down on the main screen of the PM interface.

- In the PM interface, you have the ability to register patients, work in the appointment schedule, add authorizations, and post patient charges and credits.

- In the EHR interface, you have the ability to work in individual patient charts; you will create new patient notes, prescriptions and lab orders.

Your login information is printed on the inside front cover of this book. If you change your password, please write it in the space provided on the inside front cover of this book. There is no way to retrieve your password once changed. We have also included an administrator login for your instructor on the inside back cover of the book. When you begin your class, you should cut off the card on the inside back cover of the book and give it to your instructor. If your instructor chooses, he or she can log in and view the entries that you have made in the program to check your work.

ABOUT THE EXERCISES

A *total practice management system* (TPMS) allows all tasks in a medical office to be done electronically. It is term that encompasses both (1) a PM system (which performs front-office tasks such as appointment scheduling and billing) and (2) an EHR system (which performs back-office tasks such as electronic charting and e-prescribing).

The exercises in this book are broken down into 10 modules designed to give you practice working within a TPMS, using the e-Medsys® Educational Edition. The first nine modules focus on specific tasks performed. At the beginning of each module, step-by-step instructions are given for each task. As you gain confidence and proficiency working in the program, "Putting It All Together" exercises will require you to perform the tasks without step-by-step instructions.

The last module applies the tasks you have learned in Modules 1–9 to three patient case studies.

It will take approximately 5–10 hours to complete all of the e-Medsys® exercises in this book. The time will vary depending on your computer background.

The next section, Getting Started with e-Medsys®, will help orient you to the software and provide some guidance on how to use each section prior to starting the activities.

e-Medsys® SUPPORT AND ONLINE COMPANION

For technical support related to the e-Medsys® Educational Edition, please contact Delmar Technical Support, Monday–Friday, from 8:30 a.m. to 6:30 p.m. Eastern Standard Time:

- Phone: 1-800-648-7450

- Email: delmar.help@cengage.com

Software support and additional resources for students and instructors can also be found on our Online Companion at www.delmar.cengage.com/companions. Click on "Allied Health" from the left navigation bar, and then click on the link for "The Total Practice Management Workbook: Using e-Medsys® Educational Edition." The Online Companion includes:

- Software Support: FAQ, "How To" Recorded Tutorials, Software Documentation

- Instructor Resources: Instructor Notes, Answer Key Screen Shots and Printouts

- Student Resources: Files to complete Tasks 8-3 and 8-4

INSTALLING e-Medsys® EDUCATIONAL EDITION

The e-Medsys® database and all of your work will be stored online on the TriMed Technologies server; however, you will need to follow the installation routine found at the back of this Workbook to install the e-Medsys® PM Client in order to access the program with your specific computer. You must perform this installation on every computer on which you plan to work, in order to access the program on that computer. The installation of the e-Medsys® PM Client simply allows your computer to interface with the program and the TriMed Technologies server. All data is saved online to your specific login account, so no work is lost between computers or locations. The e-Medsys® PM Client is self-contained within a single folder on your computer and only takes up 59.2 MB on your hard drive.

In order for e-Medsys® to work optimally on your computer, please ensure that you have followed all the guidelines in the System Requirements section in the back of this Workbook. Since e-Medsys® is an online program and uses pop-up windows, it is critical to follow the instructions provided for Internet settings. Some of the e-Medsys® features require third party programs like Microsoft Word and Acrobat Reader, and these are also outlined in the System Requirements section.

Instructions for uninstalling e-Medsys® Educational Edition are found at the back of this Workbook, after the installation instructions.

> **Important Note:** e-Medsys® logins will expire after 12 months after initial login. Three months prior to expiration, a notification message will display each time after logging-in.

> **Important Note:** When you are using the e-Medsys® program, a DOS Window will always be present and minimized on your taskbar. Please do not close that DOS Window or you will close the program.

USING e-Medsys® IN MULTIPLE LOCATIONS: USER SCENARIOS

Scenario #1: e-Medsys® Is Installed and Used in a School Computer Lab

The e-Medsys® program should be installed by following the installation instructions in the back of this Workbook. You must perform this installation on every computer on which students plan to work, in order for them to access the program.

Once the e-Medsys® PM Client is installed on a computer, students double click on the e-Medsys® icon and then log in to e-Medsys® with the information provided on the inside front covers of this book.

Students can work on any computer in the lab on which e-Medsys® is installed, and all work will be saved to the student's login account. No work is lost between computers.

The installation time is very quick for e-Medsys® PM Client program once the install program is downloaded. The e-Medsys® PM Client program is self-contained within a single folder. Some of the e-Medsys® PM features require third party programs like Microsoft Word and Acrobat Reader.

Due to the fact that the e-Medsys® program is self-contained, it is fairly easy for systems administrators to automate an e-Medsys® PM Client program install. If a school does re-image workstations or restores workstations to a "clean" state, it is recommended to include e-Medsys® as part of the image or "clean" state, so that the e-Medsys® PM Client program does not have to be reinstalled.

In order for e-Medsys® to work optimally on any computer, please ensure that you have followed the guidelines in the System Requirements section found at the back of this Workbook. Since e-Medsys® is an on-line program and uses pop-up windows, it is critical to follow the instructions provided for Internet settings.

Scenario #2: e-Medsys® Is Installed and Used at Student's Home

Students must follow the installation routine in the back of this Workbook, installing the e-Medsys® PM Client on their individual computer.

Once the e-Medsys® PM Client is installed on a computer, students double click on the e-Medsys® icon and then log in to e-Medsys® with the information provided on the inside front cover of this book.

Again, in order for e-Medsys® to work optimally on any computer, please ensure that you have followed the guidelines in the System Requirements section found at the back of this Workbook. Since e-Medsys® is an online program and uses pop-up windows, it is critical to follow the instructions provided for Internet settings.

Scenario #3: Student Uses e-Medsys® at School and at Home

It is easy and seamless for students to use e-Medsys® at school and at home. e-Medsys® must be installed in a computer lab, as well as on the student's home computer.

Students log in to e-Medsys® at school with the information provided on the inside front cover of this book. Students log in to e-MedSys® at home with the same login information.

All work completed at school and at home is saved to the student's login account. No work is lost between locations.

SETTING UP THE CONFIGURATION TOOL

Prior to opening the program and logging in, you must set up the Configuration Tool to configure your unique enterprise number on the computer.

1. Go to: START > ALL PROGRAMS > E-MEDSYS > E-MEDSYS CONFIGURATION

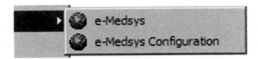

Reprinted with permission of TriMed Technologies, Corp.

2. You may receive a prompt about whether you are an e-Medsys® customer. If you do, click Yes through the prompt.

3. Type your Enterprise Number (printed on the inside cover of your book) and click OK.

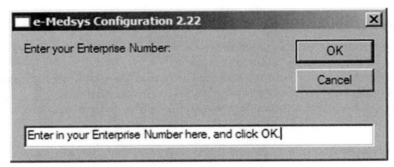

Reprinted with permission of TriMed Technologies, Corp.

4. You may receive several prompts; click Yes and OK through the prompts, until you have confirmed that the program has been configured.

5. Now, continue using the directions on Page 1 (step 2).

Getting Started with e-Medsys®

LOGGING IN, CHANGING YOUR PASSWORD, AND LOGGING OUT

Logging In to e-Medsys®

1. Set up the Configuration Tool by following the instructions on the previous page.

2. Double click the e-Medsys® icon on your desktop.

3. Enter the enterprise number, user name, and password found on the inside front cover of this workbook, and click the Login button.

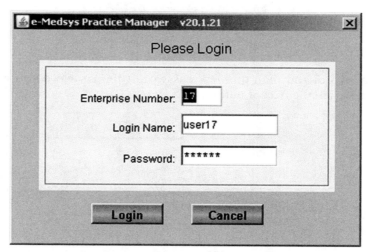

Reprinted with permission of TriMed Technologies, Corp.

4. Now you are at the e-Medsys® home page and can begin working. *Note:* In addition to the e-Medsys® home page, there will be another window open. *This window must be kept open on your desktop.* This will sometimes be referred to as "the black screen." It will always be running in the background when a user is logged in to the program.

Changing Your Password

PLEASE BE ADVISED: If you lose your password, there is no way to recover your data. If you change your password, write it in the space provided on the inside front cover of this workbook.

1. On the Main Screen Menu Bar, click File. From the drop-down menu, click Change Password.

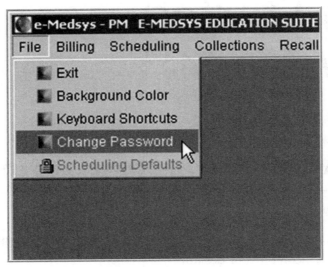

Reprinted with permission of TriMed Technologies, Corp.

2. A Change Password Utility window will open. Click the button for Change Now.

Reprinted with permission of TriMed Technologies, Corp.

3. Enter your current password, and then the new password (the password you would like to change to). When you have finished, click the Accept button.

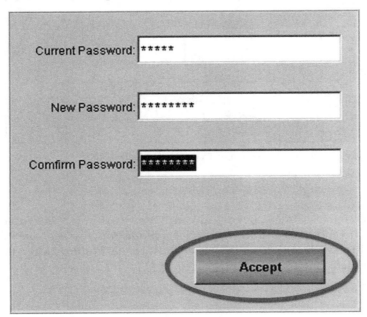

Reprinted with permission of TriMed Technologies, Corp.

4. Your password has been changed, and you will use your new password the next time you log into the program.

Logging Out of e-Medsys®

Log out by closing the software application. This is done by going to File > Exit within the application. *Note:* A warning will pop up if the user closes the application by using the X in the upper right corner.

PRACTICE MANAGEMENT INTERFACE: MAIN SCREEN MENU BAR

Clicking on a menu bar in the Practice Management interface produces a drop-down menu listing all of the functions in that module. The modules that we will use in this exercise booklet include File, Billing, Scheduling, EDI (Electronic Data Interchange), and EHR (Electronic Health Records).

Reprinted with permission of TriMed Technologies, Corp.

File Menu

The file menu allows you to log out of the program (Exit), review the keyboard shortcuts, and change your password.

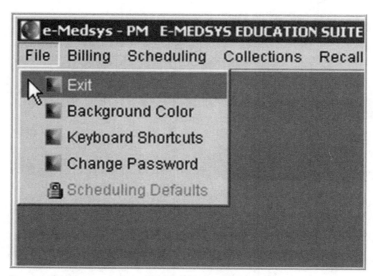

Reprinted with permission of TriMed Technologies, Corp.

Billing Menu

The billing menu allows you to work in the patient registration area, to add and update patient information, add and modify authorizations (Inquiry), post charges and credits (Posting), and other billing-related tasks.

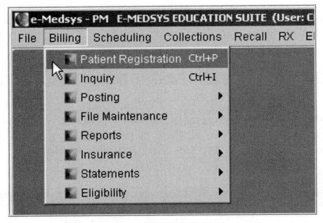

Reprinted with permission of TriMed Technologies, Corp.

Scheduling Menu

The scheduling menu allows you to work in the practice management appointment schedule (Bookings).

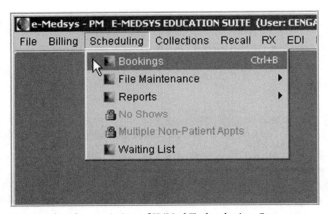

Reprinted with permission of TriMed Technologies, Corp.

Electronic Data Interchange (EDI) Menu

The EDI menu allows you to use the Charge Posting Interface. This brings over charges entered in the EHR side of the program into the payment posting section of the program (the payment posting section: Billing > Posting > Charge Posting).

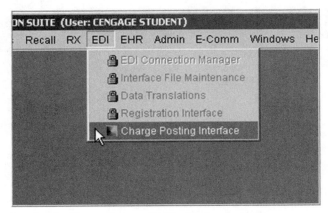

Reprinted with permission of TriMed Technologies, Corp.

EHR Menu

The EHR menu provides access to the EHR interface, to work in individual patient charts—including adding new Patient Notes, Prescriptions, Orders, and Lab Results.

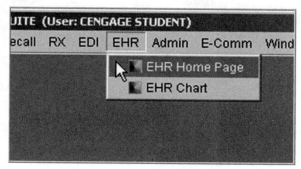

Reprinted with permission of TriMed Technologies, Corp.

Keyboard Shortcuts

Throughout the system there are default "short-cut keys" that can be used to select items from the Main Screen Menu Bar. For example, Ctrl + E is a shortcut for Exiting or Logging Out of the program. These default keys have been set up by the system:

- Ctrl + P = Patient Registration
- Ctrl + I = Inquiry
- Ctrl + B = Bookings
- Ctrl + H = Charge Posting
- Ctrl + R = Credit Posting

EHR INTERFACE: MENU BAR

Home

The home page for the EHR is the provider schedule page. All appointments made in the Practice Management interface (Scheduling > Bookings) will also appear in this schedule.

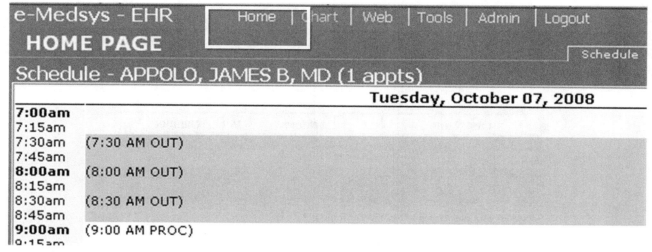

Reprinted with permission of TriMed Technologies, Corp.

Chart

Use the Chart button (on the top of the screen) to look up individual patient charts.

e-Medsys - EHR	Home	Chart	Web	Tools	Admin	Logout

PATIENT/CHART FIND

| Pat. Name: | | SSN: | | MRN: | |
| Provider: | ALL ▼ | DOB: | | ID: | |

Search   Clear   0 records found.   ☐ Open in New Window

	Patient	Pat ID	SSN	DOB	Address	City	St
A							
B							
C							

Reprinted with permission of TriMed Technologies, Corp.

FEATURES OF THE e-Medsys® PROGRAM

Enter Key or Tab Key

Using the Enter key or the Tab key on your keyboard allows you to move from field to field in the system.

Search for Items by Name

Many fields in the software can be searched by name, including patients, insurance companies, procedures, codes, and more. To search a field for an item by its name, enter the first few letters (or numbers, in the instance of a code) and press Enter on your keyboard. For example, if you want to search for patient Ashley Mansfield:

1. Enter "MAN" in the last name field and press Enter on your keyboard.

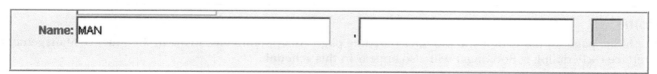

Name: MAN

Reprinted with permission of TriMed Technologies, Corp.

The software would bring up a selection window showing all patients in the system whose last name starts with those letters.

Last Name	First Name	M	Number
MANNING	LINDA		1031
MANSFIELD	ASHLEY		1036

Reprinted with permission of TriMed Technologies, Corp.

Highlight the selection by clicking on it with the mouse. Once the correct item is highlighted, you can select it in a number of ways. You can click the "OK" button, double click on the highlighted row, press the "Enter" key on your keyboard, or press Alt + O on your keyboard.

Search for Items Using Table Look-Up

Items in the software fields can also be searched for using Table Look-Up. Some of these fields include patients, procedures, diagnoses, insurance plans, and referring physicians. As an example, we will search for an Insurance Plan on the Insurance tab of the Patient Registration screen.

To bring up a list of *all* items in the program associated with a particular field:

1. Type "%" in the field and press Enter on your keyboard.

Insurance Plan: %

Reprinted with permission of TriMed Technologies, Corp.

2. The software will bring up a selection window showing all insurance plans in the system.

Insurance Plan Selection

OK | Cancel

Ins Plan	Financial Class	Address
A & I BENEFIT PLAN ADMINISTRATORS, INC.	PRIVATE INS	1220 SW MORRISON, SUITE 300
AARP	PRIVATE INS	P.O. BOX 1011
AARP	PRIVATE INS	P O BOX 13999
AETNA	AETNA PPO	P O BOX 26102
AETNA	AETNA PPO	P O BOX 129002
AETNA HMO	AETNA MANAGED CARE	P O BOX 26102
BEECH STREET	WORKERS COMP	P O BOX 57015
BLUE CROSS	BLUE CROSS	P O BOX 4152
BLUE CROSS	BLUE CROSS	P O BOX 4386
BLUE CROSS	BLUE CROSS	PO BOX 4124
BLUE CROSS OF CA	BLUE CROSS	P.O. BOX 60007
BLUE SHIELD OF CA	BLUE SHIELD	P O BOX 272510

Reprinted with permission of TriMed Technologies, Corp.

3. Highlight the correct selection and click OK (or press Enter or double click).

If you want to narrow your search down, you can type % and then the first few letters of what you are looking for. For example, if you were looking for Blue Cross, PO Box 4124, Oxnard, CA:

1. Type %BLUE and press Enter on your keyboard.

Insurance Plan: %BLUE

Reprinted with permission of TriMed Technologies, Corp.

2. The software will bring up a selection window showing all insurance plans that have "BLUE" in their name that are in the system.

Ins Plan	Financial Class	Address
BLUE CROSS	BLUE CROSS	P O BOX 4152
BLUE CROSS	BLUE CROSS	P O BOX 4386
BLUE CROSS	BLUE CROSS	PO BOX 4124
BLUE CROSS OF CA	BLUE CROSS	P.O. BOX 60007
BLUE SHIELD OF CA	BLUE SHIELD	P O BOX 272510
BLUE SHIELD OF CA	BLUE SHIELD	PO BOX 272580
BLUE SHIELD OF CA	BLUE SHIELD	P O BOX 1505

Insurance Plan Selection — OK | Cancel

Reprinted with permission of TriMed Technologies, Corp.

3. Then, highlight the correct selection and click OK (or press Enter or double click).

Entering Dates

Dates are entered in a six-digit date format (DD/MM/20YY). For the date of birth fields, the system defaults to (DD/MM/19YY). There are several shortcuts for entering dates that can be used.
When the cursor is in the date field:

1. Type a "t" to populate the field with today's date.

2. By typing 3M, the system will populate the field with the date three months from today, 6W will populate six weeks from today, 5D will populate five days from today, and so on.

Selecting Items from a Window

As mentioned previously, items can be selected in a number of ways. First, highlight the selection by clicking on it once with the mouse, and then:

1. Click the OK button; or

2. Double click on the item; or

3. Press the Enter key on the keyboard; or

4. Press Alt + O on the keyboard.

WORKING IN THE e-Medsys® PROGRAM

Patient Registration

From the Main Menu: *Billing > Patient Registration*

Exercises and step-by-step procedures covering this material are found in Module 1.

Creating a New Patient

1. Select Billing > Patient Registration from the main menu. The patient registration screen appears.

2. Click the New Patient button.

3. Enter the patient's demographic information on the Pat tab. You do not have to fill in every field with information; however, at a minimum, you must complete in the fields colored in *red*.

4. Click the Accept + Ins button if you plan to enter the patient's insurance information immediately; otherwise, click the Accept button to save the information.

Updating Patient Information

1. Select Billing > Patient Registration from the main menu. The patient registration screen appears.

2. Search for a patient by typing his or her last name in the Last Name field and clicking Search. (You can also search by date of birth, social security number, or home phone number.)

3. If there are no other patients in the database with that last name, the patient's account will populate on the screen. If there are multiple patients with that last name, highlight the patient's name on the popup window and click OK.

4. Update the new patient information by typing over previous information.

5. Click the Accept button to save the updated information.

Description of Fields on the Patient (Pat) Tab

- **Account Number:** When the New Patient button is clicked, the next chronological number is assigned automatically. The user can also key in the existing patient's account number and click the Enter key to pull up the patient's information.

- **Last Name:** Enter patient's last name with no punctuation. System will default to capital letters.

- **First Name:** Enter patient's first name with no punctuation. System will default to capital letters.

- **Address 1/Address 2:** Enter patient's address with no punctuation. Users may want to input data in all caps for uniformity throughout the system and for any merge documents or reports.

- **May Phone?:** Default is Yes. Drop-down options are Yes, No, or Special. If No or Special is selected the phone number fields become color-coded. No=Red; Special=Yellow.

- **Marital Status:** Drop-down list includes Married, Single, or Other. Options can be selected by typing in the first letter of the correct option. Other selections can be added to this default list through Billing > File Maintenance > General Codes. Select Marital Status from the drop-down menu and add more options.

- **Verify Address:** When this box is checked, a Verify Address alert window is created when patient's account is pulled up in the system.

- **Verify Phone:** When this box is checked, a Verify Phone alert window is created when patient's account is pulled up in the system.

- **Relationship to Guar:** Choose from drop-down, self, spouse, child, other.

- **User:** This field will populate based on login name.

Buttons on the Pat Tab

- **Accept Button:** Saves or updates all patient demographic information added.

- **Accept + Ins Button:** Saves or updates all patient demographic information added, and automatically takes the user into the Insurance Tab, to add the patients' insurance information.

- **History Button:** Any information changed and Accepted (saved) on a patient's account is kept in the History. Not only is the historical information available to view, but the effective dates of the information, the fields that were changed, as well as who made the changes.

Using the History Button

To view historical information that was in the system about a patient:

1. You must be in a patient's account, on the Pat tab.

2. Click the History button.

3. Highlight the selection you wish to view.

4. Click OK.

5. You will then be viewing the historical data. To get back to the Active information, click the Active button. When you are in the historical record, the Accept buttons are unavailable for you. Also the only option is to click back on the Active button to return to the Active record.

Adding an Insurance Plan to a Patient's Account

1. If you are registering a new patient and have clicked the Accept + Ins button on the Pat tab screen, the system will take you to the Insurance tab automatically.

2. Otherwise, select Billing > Patient Registration and search for a patient. (Type in the patient's last name and click Search. Select the correct patient from the pop-up window if applicable; otherwise, patient information will appear on screen automatically.)

3. Click the Ins tab.

4. Click the ADD INS button on the right side of the screen.

5. Enter the plan name in the "Insurance Plan" field. (Table Look-Up is available.)

6. Select the patient's relation to policy holder. Policy holder information fields will open up if the policy holder is someone other than "Self." Enter the policy holder information if applicable.

7. Enter the Effective Date, all group, policy, co-payment, and deductible information.

8. Click the Accept button to save changes.

Modifying an Insurance Plan

1. Select Billing > Patient Registration and search for a patient. (Type in the patient's last name and click Search. Select the correct patient from the pop-up window if applicable; otherwise, patient information will appear on screen automatically.)

2. Click the Ins tab.

3. Begin by highlighting the insurance plan you wish to modify, and click on the Modify Ins button on the right side of the screen. This will populate the insurance screen with the current information regarding the plan.

4. The plan information can now be changed. Once the correct information is entered, click Accept to save the changes made.

> **Note:** If the insurance plan address is incorrect, the plan must be inactivated and the correct plan added.

Inactivating an Insurance Plan

1. Select Billing > Patient Registration and search for a patient. (Type in the patient's last name and click Search. Select the correct patient from the pop-up window if applicable; otherwise, patient information will appear on screen automatically.)

2. Click the Ins tab.

3. Begin by highlighting the insurance plan you wish to inactivate, and click on the Modify Ins button on the right side of the screen. The system will pull forward all of the current information for the plan. This will populate the insurance screen with the current insurance information plan.

4. Uncheck the Active box in the center of the screen, and enter a valid ending date.

5. Once these changes have been made, click the Accept button to save the change.

6. The system will create an alert prompt, asking the user whether the charges should be updated. If the user answers "Yes" to this prompt, the system will make the necessary changes to the transactions posted with a date of service that falls within the effective dates of this change.

Changing the Order of an Insurance Plan

1. Select Billing > Patient Registration and search for a patient. (Type in the patient's last name and click Search. Select the correct patient from the pop-up window if applicable; otherwise, patient information will appear on screen automatically.)

2. Click the Ins tab.

3. Begin by clicking on the Change Order button on the right side of the screen. The system will then bring up an instruction window.

4. Double click on the insurance plan that should be the primary; the system will hold the new rank in the pending rank field on the left side of the screen.

5. Then double click on the insurance plan that should be the secondary.

6. The system will then rebuild the table in the new order.

7. The system will then prompt the user to update the charges with the new ranking. Click "Yes" or press the Enter key to update the charges, as appropriate.

Description of Fields on the Insurance (Ins) Tab

1. **Insurance Plan:** Table Look-Up is available. Choose the correct plan from the list.

2. **Patient's Relation to Policy Holder:** Drop-down options are Self, Spouse, Child, or Other. Select the option by typing in the first letter of the correct selection.

3. **Policy Holder Information:** Fields will open up if relation to policy holder is something other than Self.

4. **Effective Beginning Date:** Enter the date the insurance plan became effective for the charges that will be posted to this patient's account.

5. **Effective Ending Date:** Enter the date that insurance plan ended for this patient in your office. This is completed when the plan is inactivated.

6. **Co-Pay Amount:** Enter patient's co-pay. This field prints on charge ticket and will be displayed in the insurance grid throughout the system.

7. **Deductible:** Informational field. This field will be displayed in the insurance grid throughout the system.

Guarantor Information (Guar) Tab

The guarantor screen controls where the patient's statement will be sent and who is ultimately responsible for the payment on the account. The system will populate the guarantor information fields with the data that was entered in Patient Registration, Pat tab. Click on the Guarantor tab in the Patient Registration screen *if* the patient and the guarantor are different.

To add a new guarantor:

1. Select Billing > Patient Registration and search for a patient. (Type in the patient's last name and click Search. Select the correct patient from the pop-up window if applicable; otherwise, patient information will appear on screen automatically.)

2. Click the Guar tab.

3. Click on the gray Change Patient's Guar button.

4. Click on Add New Guar.

5. Enter the information for the guarantor. If the guarantor lives at the same address as the patient or shares other information, you can click the button for Copy Patient Address and Copy Patient Data.

6. Click Accept to save any changes made to the guarantor screen.

Description of Fields on the Guarantor (Guar) Tab

- **Guarantor Number:** The system will automatically assign the next available guarantor number. *Note:* This number may not match the patient account number.

- **Copy Patient Address:** Click on the gray Copy Patient Address button. The system will keep the patient address information and clear out only the first name field.

- **Copy Patient Data:** Click on the gray Copy Patient Data button. The system will keep the patient information.

- **Employment Status:** The options in the drop-down menu are Full Time, Part Time, Retired, Unemployed, and Student. The default is Full Time.

- **Patient's Relation:** Drop-down options are Self, Spouse, Child, or Other.

- **Send Mail:** Drop-down options are Yes, No, or Special. The default is Yes.

- **Dunning Message?:** If this field is checked, the patient will receive statement messages. The default is Yes.

- **Credit Card Button:** Clicking the Credit Card button will pop up the Credit Card Information screen, which allows the user to add, change, or clear credit card data.

- **Verify Address:** When the box is checked, a Verify Address alert window is created when the patient's account is pulled up in the system.

- **Verify Phone:** When the box is checked, a Verify Phone alert window is created when the patient's account is pulled up in the system.

Scheduling Appointments

From the Main Menu: *Scheduling > Bookings*

Exercises and step-by-step procedures covering this material are found in Module 2.

1. Select Scheduling > Bookings from the main menu. The scheduling screen appears.

2. Click on the Provider button. Choose the patient's provider from the "Select a Resource" pop-up window by highlighting the provider name and clicking OK.

3. Back on the scheduling screen, enter the patient's last name and press Search to bring up the patient's account. If more than one patient exists in the database with that last name, highlight the patient's name and click OK.

4. The patient's information screen is brought up; this is a snapshot of the patient's account. Click Exit to return to the scheduling screen.

5. Use the calendar icon to select the date on which the appointment should be scheduled.

6. Use the drop-down menu to select the correct Visit Type.

7. Click Book.

8. On the Supplemental Information screen, type any notes or comments about the appointment.

9. Click Clear to book another appointment. Click Exit to return to the main menu.

Patient Authorizations

From the Main Menu: *Billing > Inquiry*

Exercises and step-by-step procedures covering this material are found in Module 3.

Creating a New Authorization

1. Select Billing > Inquiry from the main menu. Search for and select the patient's name for which you wish to create a new authorization.

2. Click Authorization.

3. Click Add.

4. Fill in the type, status, request date, provider and specialty provider, and diagnosis code(s).

5. Fill in the procedure code(s) on the Authorized Visits/Procedures tab.

6. Click on the Accept button to save the authorization. (If you click on the Cancel button, all information will be lost.)

Modifying an Existing Authorization

1. Select Billing > Inquiry from the main menu. Search for and select the patient's name for which you wish to modify a new authorization.

2. Click Authorization.

3. Highlight the authorization that will be modified.

4. Click on the Modify button on the top button bar. This action will pull the user into the authorization and allow any changes to be made.

5. Once all modifications are made, click the Accept button.

To View an Existing Authorization

1. Select Billing > Inquiry from the main menu. Search for and select the patient's name for which you wish to view the authorization.

2. Click Authorization.

3. Highlight the authorization to be viewed.

4. Click the View button on the top button bar. The system will bring the user into the authorization screen in View Only Mode.

Description of Fields on the General Information Tab

- **Referral Type:** Enter referral type; options are Referral In or Referral Out.
- **Authorization Number:** Enter authorization number; this is an alphanumeric field. When the authorized procedures are posted, this number will print in box 23 on the Standard CMS-1500 form.
- **Status:** This is a drop-down field. The options are Approved, Modified, Denied, Deferred, Expired, Canceled, and Requested.
- **Request Date:** Enter the date when the authorization was requested from the insurance company.
- **Authorization Date:** Enter the date when the authorization was approved by the Insurance Company.
- **Expiration Date:** Enter the date when the authorization expires as directed by the Insurance Company. This is not a required field.
- **Primary Care Provider:** Enter the name of the primary care physician.
- **Specialty Provider:** Enter the name of the specialty physician.
- **Diagnosis:** Enter diagnosis using either ICD-9 code or description.
- **Contact:** Enter the first and last name of the contact at the insurance company. This is an informational field.

Description of Fields on the Authorized Visits/Procedures Tab

- **Specific Procedures Tab:** Enter the specific procedure(s) for the authorization. Click the appropriate radio button, to enter using a CPT or Description.
- **Quantity:** Enter the number of times this CPT code is authorized.
- **Used:** This field will populate when the specific procedure listed on the authorization is posted thru charge posting. If a specific authorized procedure is posted, the system will show the user the authorization number and count it as *used*.
- **Non-Specific Procedures:** Enter the number of times a patient can come in for nonspecific procedures for one visit. This method increments the "Used" column based on any CPT codes posted before the expiration date on the authorization.
- **Number of Visits—Office:** Enter the number of office visits authorized. The "Used" column increments based on dates of service posted with office visit codes, before the expiration date on the authorization.
- **Number of Visits—Hospital:** Enter the number of hospital visits authorized. The "Used" column increments based on dates of service posted with hospital visit codes, before the expiration date on the authorization.

Patient Reception

From the Main Menu: *Scheduling > Bookings*

Exercises and step-by-step procedures covering this material are found in Module 4.

Indicating "Arrived" and "Registered" on the Schedule

1. Select Scheduling > Bookings from the main menu. The scheduling screen appears.
2. Use the Provider button and Calendar Icon to navigate to the correct date.
3. Right click on the patient's name on the schedule, then roll the mouse over the patient's name and select Arrived.

4. The Patient Appointment Information screen is now shown. This is a snapshot of the patient's account and can be used to confirm whether registration updates need to be made.

5. If registration updates are needed, select Billing > Patient Registration. Make the necessary updates and click Accept.

6. Back on the scheduling screen, right click on the patient's name on the schedule, then roll the mouse over the patient's name and select Registered.

7. When you have finished, click the Clear button to prepare the calendar for the next entry or patient.

Printing Charge Slips

1. Select Scheduling > Bookings from the main menu. The scheduling screen appears.

2. Use the Provider button and Calendar Icon to navigate to the correct date.

3. Right click on the patient's name on the schedule, then roll the mouse over the patient's name and select Arrived.

4. This brings up Patient Appointment for the patient.

5. Click the Charge Ticket button.

6. The charge ticket will print to your local printer.

Working in the Patient Electronic Medical Record

From the Main Menu: *EHR Menu > EHR Home Page*

Exercises and step-by-step procedures covering this material are found in Module 5.

Admitting Patients Using the EHR Schedule

1. Select EHR Menu > EHR Home Page from the main menu.

2. A new browser window opens, opening the EHR interface.

3. On the right side of the screen, highlight the Provider associated with a particular patient.

4. Also on the right side of the screen, navigate to the date of the patient's appointment.

5. Now in the center of the screen, the Provider's schedule should appear, and you should see the patient's appointment on the screen if you have selected the correct date.

6. Right click on the patient's name on the schedule.

7. Roll your mouse over Status and then select Admitted.

Linking a New Patient Note to an Appointment

1. Still on the provider schedule page, again, right click on the patient's name on the schedule.

2. Select Add New (Linked) then Patient Note. Now you are in the patient's individual medical record, and a new patient note has opened on the bottom right side of the screen.

3. Fill in the date, and select the appropriate template for the patient visit. Click Save.

4. Fill in the requested information on the template. The information will depend on the template chosen, but typically includes vital signs, basic health history, and chief complaint.

5. Click Save when you have finished.

6. You may print the patient note by clicking Print > PDF Form.

Using "Tree View" to View the Patient's Chart

Tree View shows items as they are connected with one another. The Tree View will automatically build when additional items are added and linked to the patient's chart during each appointment.

1. You must be in a patient's chart to use Tree View.

2. On the lower left side of the screen, you should see a group of horizontal tabs. This is your "left navigation" bar within a patient's chart.

3. Click on APPTS. This will show all of the appointments that have been scheduled for the patient at the medical office. Make sure the box next to Tree is selected (the next step gives more explanation on Tree View).

4. Make sure the box next to Appts: Inc. Canc is *not* selected (this suppresses appointments that were cancelled).

Locating an Patient Chart without Using the EHR Schedule

1. From the menu along the top of the page, click on Chart.

2. This will bring up a search screen for finding a patient chart. You can either:

   A. Type in the patient's last name and click Enter on your keyboard; or
   B. Click the first letter of the patient's last name *C* along the left side of the screen. All patients with the last name of *C* will appear on your screen.

3. Double click the patient's name to open the patient's chart.

4. Once in the patient's chart, on the left menu, click on APPTS to prepare to link your new item to a patient appointment.

Creating Prescriptions for Provider Authorization

From the Main Menu: *EHR Menu > EHR Home Page*

Exercises and step-by-step procedures covering this material are found in Module 6.

Create a Prescription

1. When working in the EHR interface in an individual patient record, you should always *first* indicate on the EHR schedule that you have "Admitted" the patient.

2. Still on the EHR schedule page, again, right click on the patient's name on the schedule.

3. Select Add New (Linked), then select Prescription. Now you are in the patient's individual medical record, and a new prescription has opened on the bottom right side of the screen.

4. Within this tab, the provider name and the location will autopopulate based on the patient selected. Leave the Template field blank. The Folder field is autopopulated with Meds.

5. To the right of the ICD field, click on the binoculars to search for the diagnosis related to the medication being prescribed.

6. Beneath the Drug tab, in field next to Drug, enter the first three letters of the drug to be prescribed and then click on the binoculars to the right of the field. Make sure that the box to the left of Search All has a checkmark in it.

7. Scroll through the resulting list until you find the prescribed drug and dosage. Click on it. The frequency, the form, and the route of administration will autopopulate based on your selection. The category of the drug will also autopopulate.

8. Fill in the date, the quantity, and the refills of the prescription. Make sure the checkbox to the left of Current is selected.

9. Click on Save. Note that the new prescription now appears in the Tree View, beneath the today's appointment date.

Send a Prescription for Provider Sign-Off

1. With the prescription saved, and the screen still open on it, click on the open envelope in the top right corner of the template. This allows you to send a message to the provider, informing that the prescription is ready to be signed off.

2. A new window will open. On the left side of the screen, beneath "select individual staff," highlight the ADMIN entry that corresponds to your *user* login. For example, if your user login is "user15," the admin entry would be "admin15." (In a medical office setting, you would select the patient's provider in this list.)

3. With the Admin entry highlighted, click on the > button.

4. This action moves the Admin name into the Route To list. Click on this entry in the Route To list to select it.

5. Click on the radio button for Send Indiv. Action Items.

6. The Route Date and Time will autopopulate with the current date and time.

7. In the Action Type field, use the drop-down menu to select Sign Off.

8. Leave the Priority as Normal.

9. The Attachment/Routed Item is autopopulated with the prescription information.

10. Click Send.

Recording Therapeutic Injections and Immunizations

From the Main Menu: *EHR Menu > EHR Home Page*

Exercises and step-by-step procedures covering this material are found in Module 7.

Document Injections and Immunizations

1. When working in the EHR interface in an individual patient record, you should always *first* indicate on the EHR schedule that you have "Admitted" the patient.

2. Still on the EHR schedule page, again, right click on the patient's name on the schedule.

3. Select Add New (Linked) and then select Patient Note. The new note appears on the bottom right side of the screen.

4. The Provider, Department, Template Type, and Folder are autopopulated. Be sure that in the Template field None is selected.

5. Fill in the ICD field with the provider's diagnosis, and enter the date of administration.

6. In the Comments section, document the injection given.

7. Click Save.

8. When you are certain that the information documented is accurate, you will sign off on this note. Click Sign.

9. A new window opens. Enter your password (the one that you logged into e-Medsys® with) and click Save.

Complete a Charge Ticket

1. Once the patient note is saved and signed off on, you can create a charge ticket.

2. In the patient's chart, on the left side of the screen, click on the current appointment, highlighting it.

3. When you do this, the right side of the screen brings up more information regarding the appointment. From the right-hand corner of this screen, select the Superbill tab. The electronic superbill appears.

4. Enter the provider name and the date. The insurance field is autopopulated based on the patient's insurance.

5. Below the Comments section, there is a section with three tabs (Ticket, Chart, and Find). The Ticket tab is populated with some of the most common charges. If the charge is not on the Ticket tab, select the Find tab to look up a CPT code and add it to the charge ticket.

6. Type the code and then press Enter on your keyboard. Now the procedure code appears below the search field, with a box next to it. Click on the box to select it. When you do, a row at the bottom opens that indicates your selection.

7. Move your mouse into the Diag1 field. When you do, an icon of binoculars appears. Click on the binoculars. Now the cursor moves back up to the Code field. Type the first few letters of the diagnosis in the Description field and press Enter on your keyboard. Now the diagnosis code appears below the search field, with a box next to it. Click on the box to select it. When you do, note that the diagnosis code now appears in the Diag1 box at the bottom.

8. Click Save. Now you are back on the Ticket tab.

9. Enter additional CPT codes and ICD9 codes in the same manner.

10. When you are certain that the information documented is accurate, you will sign off on these charges. Click Sign.

11. A new window opens. Your sign off password is your user Login (the one you logged into e-Medsys® with; for example, "user15"). Enter your user Login and click Save.

12. You can click Print to print a copy of the Superbill.

Ordering Laboratory Tests and Entering Results

From the Main Menu: *EHR Menu > EHR Home Page*

Exercises and step-by-step procedures covering this material are found in Module 8.

Ordering Lab Tests

1. When working in the EHR interface in an individual patient record, you should always *first* indicate on the EHR schedule that you have "Admitted" the patient.

2. Still on the EHR schedule page, again, right click on the patient's name on the schedule.

3. Select Add New (Linked) and then select Order. The new Order appears on the right side of the screen.

4. The Provider, Department, Folder, and Insurance fields are autopopulated.

5. Enter the date of the order.

6. The order will be billed to the patient's insurance company, so in the Bill To option, make sure the button to the left of Insurance is selected. The Priority field has various drop-down options; select Routine. The remaining fields should be left blank.

7. Click Save.

8. Now, click on the Tests tab.

9. In the Company field, select LabCorp from the drop-down menu. The Order Set field should be autopopulated with LabCorp Test Set.

10. From the Set Tests tab, scroll down and click in the box to the left of the test that the provider is ordering.

11. Note that when you select the test, a row appears at the bottom of the screen, which indicates your selection.

12. Now click the ICD tab.

13. Type the first few letters of the diagnosis in the Desc field, and press Enter on your keyboard. This searches for all diagnosis codes in e-Medsys® that start with these letters. Click in the box to the left of the correct diagnosis code to select it.

14. Click on Save. Now the order is ready to be signed off by the provider.

Upload Laboratory Results into the Patient Chart

1. Click on EHR Home Page.

2. From the menu along the top of the page, click on Chart.

3. Search for the patient (either by typing the patient's last name and clicking Enter, or by clicking the first letter of the patient's last name along the left side of the screen). Double click on the patient's name to open his chart.

4. From the left navigational tab, click on APPTS.

5. Find the correct appointment and the linked Order for lab testing.

6. Right click on the correct Order. Select Add New (Linked) and then select Upload File. The Document upload appears on the right side of the screen.

7. Folder: Select Results from the drop-down menu.

8. Doc. Type: Select Lab Result Report from the drop-down menu.

9. In the ICD field, click the binoculars and search for the provider's diagnosis (*hint:* type the first few letters of the diagnosis in the description field and press Enter).

10. Enter the date.

11. In the name field, enter Lab Result Report if not already populated.

12. Next to the Document to Upload field, click Browse. Locate and select the laboratory results file on your computer.

13. Click Upload to Chart.

14. Now, on the left side of the screen, the Lab Result should appear in Tree View, as a submenu item beneath the corresponding Order.

Posting Charges and Payments at the Time of Service

From the Main Menu: *Billing > Posting > Charge Posting*

Exercises and step-by-step procedures covering this material are found in Module 9.

What Does Batch Posting Mean?

Batch Posting allows a user to have multiple open posting batches available at one time. This is a tool for organizing the transactions posted in the practice.

> **FOR EXAMPLE:** *One batch for posting a large Blue Cross EOB and another batch for patient payments and yet another batch for Charges for a specific doctor or a specific day.*

Creating a New Batch Posting

1. When you select Billing > Posting > Charge Posting, a Batch Window opens. This window shows all open batches and gives the user a chance to open a new batch or post to an existing batch.

2. To open a new batch, click on the New Batch button.

3. Populate the Open Date (the date the batch was opened; the system will default to the current date), the Batch Description, and the Department (indicates the *physical location* of the department the user is posting from).

4. Click OK. Now you are on the Charge Posting screen and can enter account charges.

Posting Charges to an Existing Batch

1. When you select Billing > Posting > Charge Posting, a Batch Window opens. This window shows all open batches and gives the user a chance to open a new batch or post to an existing batch.

2. To post new charges to an existing batch, highlight the batch that you wish to post charges to, and click OK.

3. Now you are on the Charge Posting screen and can enter account charges.

Posting Charges

1. Search for (type in the patient's last name and click Search) and select the patient for which you wish to post charges.

2. Press OK to accept Charge Ticket number if correct, or Cancel if there is no Charge Ticket number. If a Charge Ticket was created, the system will populate the Date, Department, and Provider.

3. Now your cursor appears in the Charge Tab, in the Date field. Enter the date of service, department, and provider for the charge (if not already populated).

4. Enter the first procedure code from the patient's visit. You can search for a CPT code using Table Look-Up (%).

5. Enter the diagnosis code from the patient's visit. You can search for an ICD-9 code using Table Look-Up (%). Once the primary diagnosis is entered, the Additional Diagnosis tab will allow for the entering of up to three additional diagnoses. Enter additional diagnosis codes if appropriate.

6. Click OK to record the charges. The charges now appear in the Charge Accumulation box that holds the charges (and allows you to enter additional procedures) until you are ready to post the entire visit's charges to the patient's account.

7. On the bottom of the screen, there are four boxes:

   - Check the box next to Credits to inform the system a payment needs to be posted after charges have been posted. Once the charges have been accepted, the system will automatically open the credit posting screen using the same batch. When the payment is entered and accepted, the system will take the user back to the charge posting screen.
   - Check the boxes next to Prt Statement to indicate that a statement should be produced for this patient after charges and payments have been posted.
   - Check the box next to Prt Receipt to inform the system that a receipt should be produced for this patient only for those charges and payments posted today.
   - Check the box next to Prt Claim if you would like to print a CMS-1500 form of the patient's visit, after the charges.

8. When you have recorded all charges and are ready to post them to the patient's account, click the Accept button. If you have checked the box next to Credits, the system will take you to the Credit Posting screen.

Correcting Charges Prior to Posting

1. If an incorrect charge was entered in the Charge Accumulation box; double click on the transaction in question, click on the Clear Line button. This action will clear the transaction from the Charge Accumulation box.

2. Follow the steps for Posting Charges and enter the correct values. Click OK to record the charges back to the Charge Accumulation box.

3. When you have recorded all charges and are ready to post them to the patient's account, click the Accept button.

Description of Fields on the Charge Tab

- **Date:** Enter the date of service for the charge.

- **Department, Provider, Primary Financial Class, Referring Provider:** These fields default to the entries from patient registration.

- **Procedure:** Search by CPT code by entering a "%" or entering the first digit of the code, or enter the first few digits of the code, if known.

- **Dx1:** Search for an ICD code by entering % or entering the first digit of the code, or enter the first few digits of the code, if known.

- **Charge Amount:** The system will automatically populate with the correct fee.

- **Return to Date of Service:** Check this box if the cursor should be positioned in the date field after each charge line is posted. This box would be checked if posting multiple services are done on different dates, for example, hospital charges.

- **Update Dx:** Click on the Update Dx button to indicate the primary diagnosis as the default diagnosis for that patient.

- **Credits:** Check this box to inform the system a payment needs to be posted after charges have been posted. Once the charges have been accepted, the system will automatically open the credit posting screen using the same batch. When the payment is entered and accepted, the system will take the user back to the charge posting screen.

- **Prt Stmt:** Check this box to inform the system a demand statement should be produced for this patient after charges and payments have been posted.

- **Prt Receipt:** Check this box to inform the system that a receipt should be produced for this patient only for those charges and payments posted today.

- **Prt Claim:** Check this box to inform the system a demand claim form should be produced for this patient after charges and payments have been posted.

Posting Payments at the Time of Service

1. When you Accept the charges on the Charge Posting screen, the system will automatically bring the patient from charge posting forward into the credit-posting screen. The system will automatically default to the same batch, the same date of service, and it will default the credit type to a patient type payment.

2. Enter the credit type (Cash, Check, Credit Card).

3. Enter check information (check number and ABA number) if check is the method of payment.

4. Enter the amount of the payment.

5. Patient payments are posted to the patient's outstanding transactions using the Patient, Today, **All Open**, or All radio button.

   - To apply payments to Today's charges, click the radio button next to Today.
   - To apply payments to other outstanding charges, select the radio button next to All Open.

6. When you select a radio button, an itemized list will appear below with open patient charges (either today's charges or all open charges, depending on what you selected).

7. In the Applied column, enter the amount that is to be applied to each charge.

8. Click Accept to save the payment to the patient's account.

Description of Fields on the Credits Tab

- **S:** Enter default to "Yes" to have transactions appear on patient's statement.

- **Patient Radio Button:** Displays all charges with a patient remaining balance.

- **Today's Radio Button:** Displays all of today's charges with a remaining balance.

- **All Open Radio Button:** Displays all outstanding charges with a remaining balance (patient responsible and insurance responsible). This radio button is normally used for posting patient payments.

- **All:** Displays all charges; even charges with a zero remaining balance.

- **Apply:** Enter charges to the line item or items. Be sure to press Enter key to apply the payment to the last transaction.

- **Auto Pay:** After you enter the amount and choose the "All Open" radio button, you can click on the Auto Pay button, which will automatically apply the payment to the oldest outstanding charge.

- **Statement:** Check the box to produce an itemized statement. When the payment has been "Accepted," the statement will print on the default printer.

- **Receipt:** Check the box to produce a receipt for the patient including only transactions posted today. When the payment has been "Accepted," the receipt will print on the default printer.

Posting Charges Using the EDI Feature

From the Main Menu: *EDI > Charge Posting Interface*

Exercises and step-by-step procedures covering this material are found in Module 9.

1. When you select EDI > Charge Posting Interface, an Interface Charges window appears.

2. Select a provider (or all providers) and date parameters. The system will look for charges for that provider and date parameters.

3. Click Search.

4. The system will bring up all patients with charges meeting the search criteria you selected.

5. Highlight the patient's name for which you would like to post charges, and click OK.

6. Now, create a new batch or select an existing batch to which to post the charges.

7. The system will move all the charge information to the Charge Posting screen.

8. Check the boxes next to Credits, Prt Statement, Prt Receipt, and Prt Claim, if appropriate.

9. Click Accept.

Patient Registration

In this module, you will:

1. Register new patients.

2. Modify insurance plan information associated with an established patient's account.

3. Change the order of an insurance plan on an established patient's account.

4. Inactivate an insurance plan associated with an established patient's account.

TASK 1-1: ENTERING PATIENT DEMOGRAPHICS

Today is October 6, 2008. Elizabeth Greenley, a friend of patient Linda Manning, has been looking for a new provider. Linda suggests that she make an appointment with her provider, Harriet Medusa, MD, Gastro Calabasas Medical Group, 23901 Calabasas Rd, Suite 1064, in Calabasas, phone (918) 591-0081.

Elizabeth decides to contact the office today to set up an appointment with Dr. Medusa. Table 1-1 lists registration information that was provided by Elizabeth.

1. Log in to e-Medsys®.

2. At the top of the screen, click on Billing.

3. Click on Patient Registration from the drop-down box. (You can also get to this screen by pressing Ctrl + P on the keyboard.) The Patient Registration screen will appear.

TABLE 1-1: Registration Information for Elizabeth Greenley

Patient Information

Patient Name	Elizabeth K. Greenley
DOB	09/28/1956
SSN	021-80-1981
Marital Status	Married
Home Address	345 Sea Breeze Lane Calabasas, CA 91303
Phone Numbers	Home: (818) 338-5436 Work: (818) 737-3200 x25 Cell Phone: (818) 537-2077 The patient said that it is OK to call her at any of these numbers. The patient said that it is OK to leave a message at any of these numbers.
Email Address	EKG@hotmail.com
Employer	Caring Health Center

Emergency Contact Information

Name	Robert W. Greenley
Phone	(818) 357-9989

Guarantor Information

Name	Robert W. Greenley
DOB	03/10/1956
SSN	026-31-5887
Home Address	Same as Patient
OK to send mail?	Yes
Phone Numbers	Home: (818) 338-5436 Work: (818) 781-2276 x345 Cell: (818) 357-9989
Email	rgreenley@zero.net
Employer	Hanover Plastic Corporation

Insurance Information

Carrier	Aetna PPO PO Box 129002 San Diego, CA 92112
Effective Date of Plan	7/1/2008
Subscriber	Robert W. Greenley
Group Number	HPC01
Policy Number	RG026315887
Co Pay Amount	$10
Deductible Amount	none

Practice Information

Physician	Dr. Medusa
Department	Gastro Calabasas Medical Group

4. Click the New Patient button (note that in the Account Number field, the next chronological number is assigned automatically by the program). Use the information found in Table 1-1 to complete the following steps. In the e-Medsys® program, the field names in *red* indicate required fields. The other fields are additional information that can be added.

5. Enter the patient's last name, first name, and middle initial. Note that here the system will default to capital letters.

6. Enter the patient's address, with no punctuation. To maintain continuity, we recommend turning the CAPS LOCK button on.

7. Enter the patient's zip code. Once entered, the city and state will automatically populate in those fields.

8. Enter the patient's e-mail address.

9. Enter the patient's employer name.

10. Enter the patient's home phone, area code first, with no spaces or dashes. Continue to add the patient's work and cell phone numbers in the same manner.

11. Enter the patient's emergency contact name and phone number.

12. The patient has indicated that she may be contacted by phone, so check YES in this field, if not already selected. Note that if the patient had not agreed to be contacted by phone, be sure NO is selected in this field.

13. Select the patient's marital status from the drop-down box.

14. Leave the field for the patient's driver's license number blank. This is sometimes required as it could be helpful information in tracking down patients through the Department of Motor Vehicles (DMV) if they become delinquent in their payments or cannot otherwise be located.

15. Enter the patient's social security number, with no spaces or dashes.

16. Enter the patient's date of birth. Press the Enter key, which calculates the patient's age automatically.

17. Select Female, for the patient's sex.

18. From the Department drop-down, select Gastro Calabasas Medical Group, since that is where the patient will be seen.

19. From the Provider drop-down, select Dr. Harriet Medusa.

20. Leave the Referred By field blank. If there was a referring provider, you would enter the appropriate name in this field.

21. Leave the First Seen, After Care, and Misc fields blank. The patient has not been seen yet.

22. Uncheck the boxes next to Verify Address and Verify Phone if checked. When these are selected, an alert pop-up window will appear each time the patient's account is pulled up. Keeping current with both the address and the phone number is important because the office may have to contact the patient either via the phone or through the mail. Each practice will have a preference whether to verify contact information each time the patient's account is accessed to make sure the information is up-to-date.

23. From the Relation to Guar drop-down, select Spouse.

24. Check your work with the following screen shot.

Reprinted with permission of TriMed Technologies, Corp.

25. When you are finished, click on Accept + Ins button. This action saves all of your entries on the Patient tab, and then opens the Insurance tab, to continue registering the patient. Proceed directly to Task 1-2.

TASK 1-2: ENTERING INSURANCE PLAN INFORMATION

Now that you have created a new record for the patient Elizabeth Greenley and have entered her demographic information, her insurance plan information can be added. Continue to use the information given in Table 1-1.

1. Click on the Add Ins button on the right side of the screen.

Reprinted with permission of TriMed Technologies, Corp.

2. In the Insurance Plan field, type Aetna, and then press the Enter key. An Insurance Plan pop-up window will appear. Highlight the Aetna PPO in San Diego.

Ins Plan	Financial Class	Address	City	ST	Zip
AETNA	AETNA PPO	P O BOX 26102	GREENSBORO	NC	27402
AETNA	AETNA PPO	P O BOX 129002	SAN DIEGO	CA	92112
AETNA HMO	AETNA MANAGED CARE	P O BOX 26102	GREENSBORO	NC	27402

Reprinted with permission of TriMed Technologies, Corp.

3. Click OK.

4. In the Policy Holder information box, in the Patient's Relation to the Policy Holder field, select Spouse from the drop-down menu. When you do, note that some of the fields autopopulate.

5. In the Name fields, enter GREENLEY, ROBERT W. Enter the remainder of the information for this area using the information given in Table 1-1. Check your work with the following screen shot.

Reprinted with permission of TriMed Technologies, Corp.

6. Tab over to the Effective Date field, and enter 7/1/2008 in the first field. This is the date the insurance plan became effective for the charges that will be posted to the patient's account. Leave the second field blank, as the plan is still effective. This will be completed when the plan is inactivated in the system.

7. Enter the Group Number and Policy Number in the appropriate fields.

8. Enter the patient's co-pay amount in the appropriate field. The co-pay amount will print on charge tickets. (Both the co-pay and deductible amounts will be displayed in the insurance grid throughout the system.)

9. Leave the boxes next to Accept Assign. and Sig. on File checked. Check your work with the following screen shot.

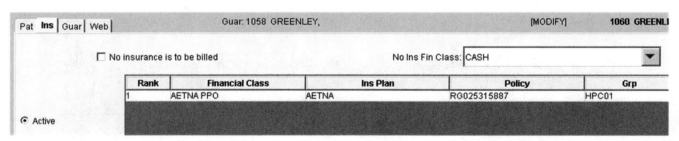

Reprinted with permission of TriMed Technologies, Corp.

10. Click Accept. Now, the insurance plan is listed in the top table for the patient. Also note that the box next to "No Insurance is to be billed" is now unchecked, as there is now an insurance in the system.

| Pat | **Ins** | Guar | Web | | | Guar: 1058 GREENLEY, | | [MODIFY] | 1060 GREENLI |

| | No insurance is to be billed | | No Ins Fin Class: CASH | | ▼ |

Rank	Financial Class	Ins Plan	Policy	Grp
1	AETNA PPO	AETNA	RG025315887	HPC01

● Active

Reprinted with permission of TriMed Technologies, Corp.

11. Click Exit at the top of the screen.

TASK 1-3: SEARCHING FOR A PATIENT AND UPDATING GUARANTOR INFORMATION

In this task, you will learn how to search for an existing patient in the office's database and update registration information. In this case, you will update guarantor information, which provides information as to where the patient's statement will be sent and who is the responsible party regarding the payment on the account. The Guarantor Information tab is used only if the patient and the guarantor are not the same individual. If the patient is the guarantor, the system will automatically populate the guarantor information fields with the data that was entered in the other patient registration screens.

1. At the top of the screen, click on the Billing.

2. Click on Patient Registration from the drop-down box. The Patient Registration screen will appear.

3. Enter GREENLEY in the Last Name field, and then click the Search button.

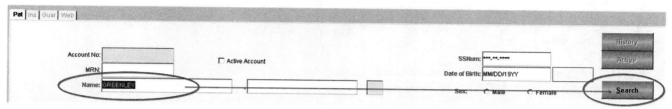

Reprinted with permission of TriMed Technologies, Corp.

4. Now, Elizabeth Greenley's patient record appears on the screen. Select the Guar tab (Guarantor tab).

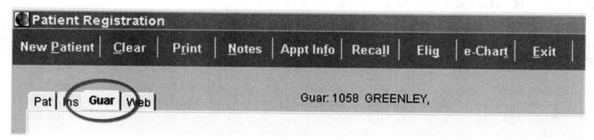

Reprinted with permission of TriMed Technologies, Corp.

5. Use the date from Table 1-1 to fill in the empty fields. Double check the fields to be sure all of Robert's information is correct; make changes as necessary.

6. Robert Greenley has given permission to send mail, so select YES from the Send Mail drop-down list, if not already selected.

7. Be sure the boxes next to "Dunning Message?" and "Send Statement to Guarantor" are checked. Check your work with the following screen shot.

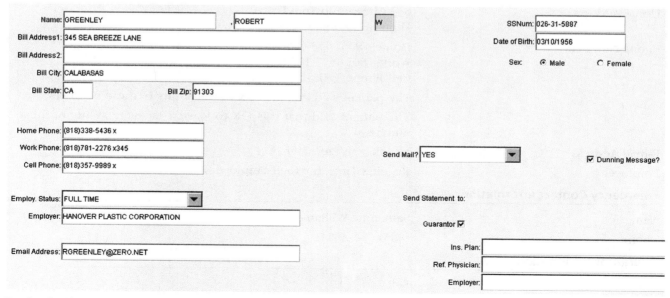

Reprinted with permission of TriMed Technologies, Corp.

8. When you have finished, click Accept.

9. Click Clear to exit out of Elizabeth's account, but still continue to work in the Patient Registration area.

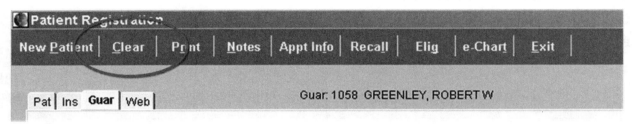

Reprinted with permission of TriMed Technologies, Corp.

PUTTING IT ALL TOGETHER

TASK 1-4: REGISTERING A NEW PATIENT

This task requires you to register a patient without step-by-step instructions as given in previous tasks. Use the information in Table 1-2 to register Reggie Williams.

Today is October 8, 2008. Reggie Williams has been referred by his aunt, Marge Demo, to the office of James B. Appolo, M.D., of the Gastro Calabasas Medical Group, located on 23901 Calabasas Road, Suite 1064, Calabasas, CA 91302, phone 818-591-0081. He has been experiencing some bloating and abdominal pain for the past few weeks. Table 1-2 lists registration information that was provided by Reggie.

TABLE 1-2: Registration Information for Reggie Williams	
Patient Information	
Patient Name	Reginald A. Williams
DOB	04/10/1967
SSN	056-11-7834
Marital Status	Single
Home Address	631 Cherry Blossom Drive Ventura, CA 93001
Phone Numbers	Home: (805) 543-6786 Work: (805) 537-1274 Cell Phone: (805) 525-8002
	The patient said that it is OK to call at any of these numbers.
	The patient said that it is OK to leave a message at any of these numbers.
E-mail Address	middleman@zero.net
Employer	Reggie's Tires, Inc (Self-Employed)
Emergency Contact Information	
Name	Samantha Williams
Phone	(805) 786-2864
Guarantor Information	
Name	Self

TABLE 1-2:   Registration Information for Reggie Williams (continued)

Insurance Information

Carrier	Blue Shield of CA PO Box 1505 Red Bluff, CA 96080
Effective Date of Plan	02/01/2006
Subscriber	Self
Group Number	None
Policy Number	323776880
Co-Pay Amount	$10
Deductible Amount	None

Practice Information

Physician	Dr. Apollo
Department	Gastro Calabasas Medical Group

TASK 1-5: CHANGING THE ORDER OF PATIENT INSURANCE PLANS

Marge Demo is a current patient in the database. Her primary insurance plan has been Blue Shield of CA (policy number 3321479879). Mutual of Omaha will now become her primary plan (policy number 654789797; group number TYRT8583084).

1. Log in to e-Medsys®.

2. At the top of the screen, click on Billing.

3. Click on Patient Registration from the drop-down box. The Patient Registration screen will appear.

4. Search for Marge Demo's account, by typing DEMO in the last name field, and clicking the Search button.

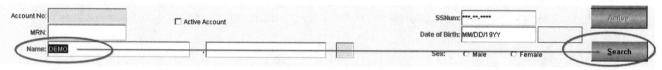

Reprinted with permission of TriMed Technologies, Corp.

5. Highlight Marge Demo's name on the Patient Search screen and click OK. (This screen appears when there is more than one patient who fits the search criteria. If there is only one patient who fits the search criteria, the program automatically brings the patient's account on the Patient Registration screen without this step.)

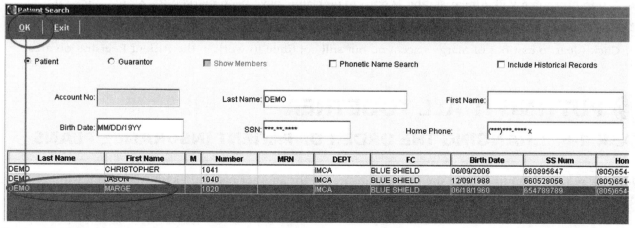

Reprinted with permission of TriMed Technologies, Corp.

6. Now Marge's information appears in the Patient Registration screen. Click on the Insurance tab.

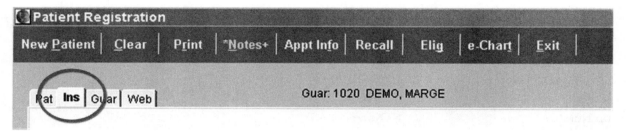

Reprinted with permission of TriMed Technologies, Corp.

7. Click on the Change Order button on the right side of the screen. A pop-up window appears, giving the direction to double click on each row in the new order. Click OK.

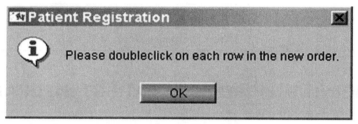

Reprinted with permission of TriMed Technologies, Corp.

8. Now double click on the row for Mutual of Omaha, and then double click on the row for Blue Shield of CA. A pop-up window appears, noting that the Insurance table will be rebuilt in the new order you have just selected. Click OK.

9. A pop-up window appears, asking to update the patient's charges with the new insurance ranking?

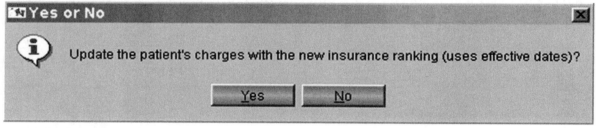

Reprinted with permission of TriMed Technologies, Corp.

10. Click Yes.

11. A pop-up screen will appear stating "Appropriate claims have been marked for rebill." Click OK.

12. The change in the insurance order is now complete.

13. Click Clear to exit out of Marge's account, but still continue to work in the Patient Registration area.

PUTTING IT ALL TOGETHER

TASK 1-6: CHANGING THE ORDER OF PATIENT INSURANCE PLANS

This task requires you to change the order of insurance for another patient, Victor Ackerman, without step-by-step instructions as given in the previous task.

1. Victor Ackerman has had Medicare as his primary insurance, Policy Number 648789794A. His Blue Shield of CA will now become his primary, Policy Number 6547897414, Group Number WR68045.

TASK 1-7: INACTIVATING A PATIENT'S INSURANCE

Diane Bollinger has decided to leave her position as head cashier at Val's Surf Shop and return to school to further her education. As such, she will lose her insurance coverage and her Blue Shield of CA plan will terminate as of 11/01/2008.

1. Log in to e-Medsys®.

2. At the top of the screen, click on Billing.

3. Click on Patient Registration from the drop-down box. The Patient Registration screen will appear.

4. Search for Diane Bollinger's account, by typing "Bollinger" in the last name field, and clicking the Search button.

5. The patient's account is automatically brought on the Patient Registration screen (as there are no other patients registered with Bollinger as the last name). Click on the Insurance tab.

6. The patient's insurance information is displayed in the top table. Click on the row, Blue Shield of CA, to select the insurance to be inactivated. Click on the Modify Ins button on the right side of the screen.

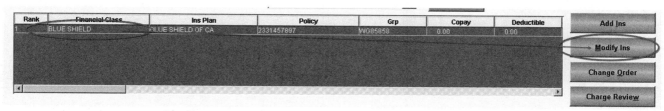

Reprinted with permission of TriMed Technologies, Corp.

7. Now, the bottom of the screen is populated with the plan information. Uncheck the box next to Active in the center of the screen, and then enter the Ending Effective Date, 11/01/2008.

Reprinted with permission of TriMed Technologies, Corp.

8. Click the Accept button once all the changes have been made to save the information.

9. A pop-up screen appears with the question "Update the patient's charges with the new insurance ranking (uses effective dates)?" Click Yes.

10. The system will now make the necessary changes to the transactions that were posted with a date of service that falls within the effective dates of the changes. The plan will no longer show as active but will be part of the history and can be seen by selecting the Inactive View mode. (To do this, select the radio button next to Inactive on the left side of the screen.)

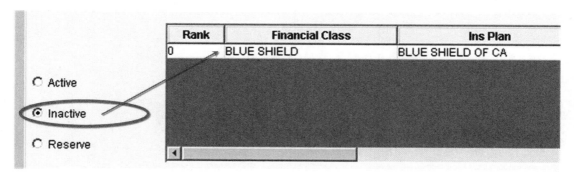

Reprinted with permission of TriMed Technologies, Corp.

11. Click Clear to exit out of Diane's account, but still continue to work in the Patient Registration.

🌑 PUTTING IT ALL TOGETHER

TASK 1-8: INACTIVATING A PATIENT'S INSURANCE

This task requires you to inactivate the insurance of another patient, Diane Brown, without step-by-step instructions as given in the previous task. When you are finished, click Exit on the top of the Patient Registration screen to return to the main menu.

1. Diane Brown is in the process of changing jobs. She will lose her current coverage with Regence (Regence Choice Plan) on 10/31/2008. Her coverage with a new carrier will not start for another 60 days.

Scheduling

In this module, you will:

1. Schedule appointments and procedures for new and established patients.

2. Cancel and reschedule appointments.

TASK 2-1: SCHEDULING AN APPOINTMENT FOR A NEW PATIENT

Today is October 6, 2008. Elizabeth Greenley is a new patient of Dr. Medusa and would like to schedule an annual exam. She would prefer an appointment at 10:15 a.m. on Thursday, October 16.

1. Log in to e-Medsys®.

2. At the top of the screen, click on Scheduling.

3. Click on Bookings from the drop-down box. (You can also get to this screen by pressing Ctrl + B [the shortcut command] on the keyboard.)

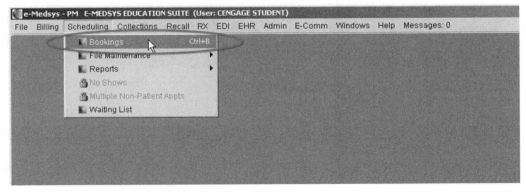

Reprinted with permission of TriMed Technologies, Corp.

4. The Appointment Scheduling screen will now appear. Note that the scheduling screen is currently showing Dr. James Appolo's schedule. (Dr. Appolo is the default provider.)

5. Click on the Provider button that appears in the left-hand corner of the screen. This will allow you to change to another provider's schedule.

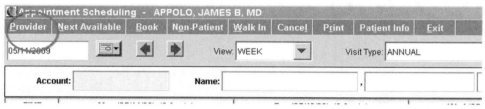

Reprinted with permission of TriMed Technologies, Corp.

6. A pop-up screen, Select A Resource(s), will appear. Highlight Elizabeth's provider from the physician column, Dr. Medusa.

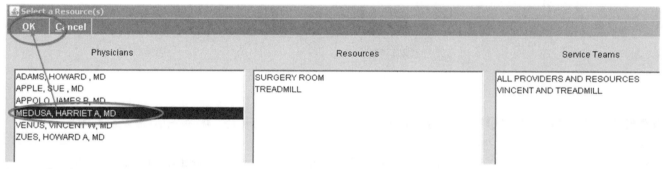

Reprinted with permission of TriMed Technologies, Corp.

7. Once the provider's name is highlighted, click OK. Now the Appointment Scheduling screen shows Dr. Medusa's schedule.

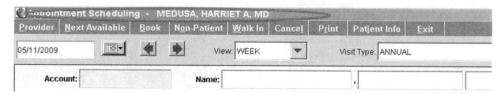

Reprinted with permission of TriMed Technologies, Corp.

8. In the Name field, enter Greenley, Elizabeth. Now click on the Search button on the right side of the screen.

Reprinted with permission of TriMed Technologies, Corp.

9. Now the Patient Appointment Information is brought up. This screen is a snapshot of the patient's account. The top tab fields show basic patient information such as contact information, guarantor information, and whether the patient has any outstanding balances. The bottom area shows any previously scheduled appointments, if applicable. Elizabeth is a new patient, so this area is empty. Click Exit to return to the Calendar screen. Note that now Elizabeth's information is populated at the top of the screen.

10. In the top middle of the screen, there is a drop-down field for Visit Type. The default visit type is Annual (Annual exam), which is what Elizabeth's appointment is, so this can be left as is.

11. Click date field, in the upper left corner, beneath the Provider button. (This field automatically defaults to today's date.)

Reprinted with permission of TriMed Technologies, Corp.

12. Type 10/16/2008 and press Enter on the keyboard.

13. The week of the chosen date now appears on the screen.

14. Dr. Medusa may be scheduled for any type of appointment on October 16, 2008, which is indicated by ANY in the appointment slots. On the weekly appointment calendar, highlight the requested time slot, 10:15 a.m. by single clicking on it.

Thu (10/16/08) (0 Appts)
GASTCA OUT
GASTCA OUT
GASTCA OUT
GASTCA OUT
GASTCA OUT
GASTCA OUT
GASTCA ANY
GASTCA ANY
GASTCA ANY
GASTCA ANY
GASTCA ANY
GASTCA ANY
GASTCA ANY
GASTCA ANY
GASTCA ANY
GASTCA ANY
GASTCA ANY
GASTCA OUT
GASTCA OUT
GASTCA OUT
GASTCA OUT
GASTCA OUT
GASTCA OUT
GASTCA OUT
GASTCA ANY
GASTCA ANY
GASTCA ANY
GASTCA ANY
GASTCA ANY
GASTCA ANY
GASTCA ANY
GASTCA ANY
GASTCA ANY
GASTCA ANY
GASTCA ANY
GASTCA ANY
GASTCA ANY

Reprinted with permission of TriMed Technologies, Corp.

15. Click Book from the menu at the top of the screen.

16. A Supplemental Information screen will appear. Type ANNUAL EXAM in the Reason for Visit field. Note at the bottom of the screen that the system has instructions that should be given to the patient for this type of appointment.

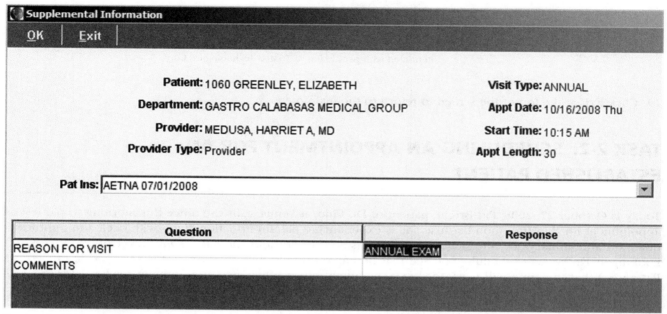

17. Click OK. The appointment is now booked on the weekly calendar for Dr. Medusa. If you hover your mouse over the appointment slot, detailed information about the appointment will appear.

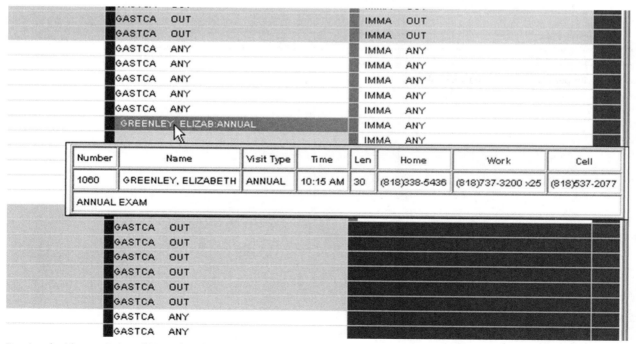

18. Now that the appointment is booked, click the Clear button at the top right side of the screen to be prepared to book another appointment.

Reprinted with permission of TriMed Technologies, Corp.

19. Click Exit at the top of the screen to return to the main menu.

TASK 2-2: SCHEDULING AN APPOINTMENT FOR AN ESTABLISHED PATIENT

Today is October 27, 2008. Pat Bright, patient of Dr. Vincent Venus, calls the office this morning to request an appointment for this afternoon because she is experiencing painful urination along with back and right lower quadrant abdominal pain. She states her urine has a foul odor and she has a slight fever of 100.1°F (37°C). Looking at Dr. Venus's schedule, you see that he has reserved time at 2:00 p.m. for any type of office visit. Pat agrees that this time will work for her. Schedule a return office visit appointment for her later today, at 2:00 p.m.

1. Log in to e-Medsys®, if not already logged in.

2. At the top of the screen, click on Scheduling. Click on Bookings from the drop-down box.

3. View Dr. Venus's weekly appointment schedule by clicking the Provider button at the top left corner, and then selecting Dr. Venus.

4. Select today's date by clicking in the date field. Type 10/27/2008 and press Enter on the keyboard. The week of the chosen date now appears on the screen.

5. Now search for Pat Bright. In the Name field, enter BRIGHT and click Search.

Reprinted with permission of TriMed Technologies, Corp.

6. Pat Bright's appointment history appears on the screen. When scheduling established patients, this screen can be used to confirm the correct patient is being booked. It is also a snapshot of the patient's account. Click Exit to return to the main Appointment screen. Pat Bright's information is now populated across the top of the schedule.

| Account: 1004 | | Name: BRIGHT | | , PAT | | SS#: 222-34-7897 | DOB: 04/12/1936 |

Reprinted with permission of TriMed Technologies, Corp.

7. From the Visit Type drop-down, select return office visit (Ret OV).

8. Click on the 2:00-p.m. slot on the calendar for October 27, and click the Book button.

9. On the Supplemental Information screen, in the REASON FOR VISIT field, type: PAINFUL URINATION; BACK AND ABDOMINAL PAIN.

10. In the COMMENTS field, type: PATIENT STATES URINE HAS FOUL ODOR; TEMP IS 100.1F.

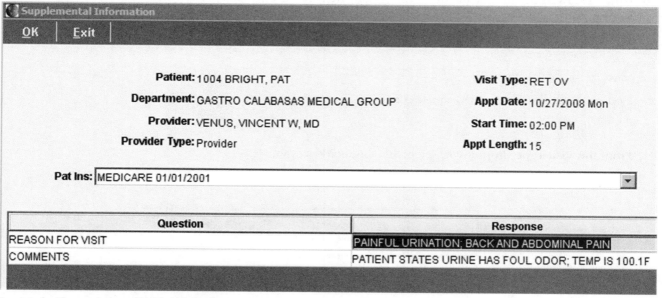

Reprinted with permission of TriMed Technologies, Corp.

11. After giving Pat the instructions on the Supplemental Information screen, click OK. Pat's appointment now appears on the schedule.

12. Now that the appointment is booked, click Clear at the top right side of the screen to be prepared to book another appointment.

TASK 2-3: SCHEDULING A PROCEDURE FOR AN ESTABLISHED PATIENT

Perry Marshall, a patient of Dr. Venus, has a history of diverticulosis. At his last visit, he was instructed to make an appointment for a sigmoidoscopy, which he does before leaving the office. Schedule an appointment (Visit Type: SIG) for Monday, November 17, 2008 at 9:30 a.m. for the 30-minute procedure.

1. Log in to e-Medsys®, if not already logged in. At the top of the screen, click on Scheduling. Click on Bookings from the drop-down box.

2. View Dr. Venus's weekly appointment schedule by clicking the Provider button at the top left corner, and then selecting Dr. Venus.

3. Select the date by using the calendar icon.

4. Now search for Perry Marshall. In the Name field, enter Marshall and click Search.

5. Perry has a Collections Alert in the system; click OK to close the reminder.

> **Note:** The e-Medsys® program includes built-in reminders, such as this one. For the purposes of these exercises, we will click through the system reminders.

6. Now Perry's appointment history appears on the screen. Click Exit to return to the main appointment screen. Perry's information is now populated across the top of the schedule.

Reprinted with permission of TriMed Technologies, Corp.

7. From the Visit Type drop-down, select SIG (sigmoidoscopy).

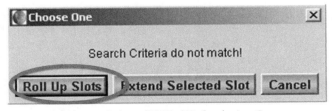

Reprinted with permission of TriMed Technologies, Corp.

8. Click on the 9:30 a.m. slot on the calendar for November 17, and click the Book button.

9. A pop-up window appears, informing the user that the appointment slot does not match the criteria selected. This feature helps remind users to book appointment visit types as indicated on the scheduler to ensure a smooth patient flow. However, this particular appointment slot indicates that ANY appointment type may be booked, so it is all right to go ahead and book the slot. Click the button for Roll Up Slots.

Reprinted with permission of TriMed Technologies, Corp.

10. On the Supplemental Information screen, in the REASON FOR VISIT field, type: SIGMOIDOSCOPY.

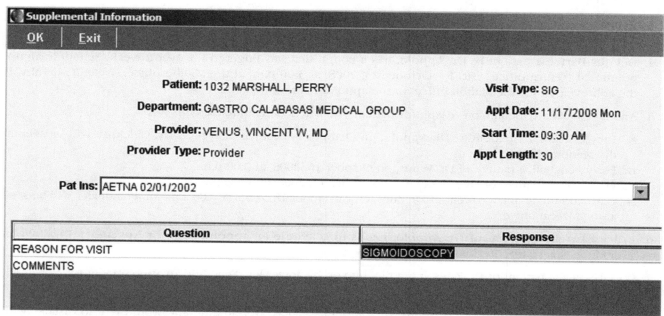

Reprinted with permission of TriMed Technologies, Corp.

11. After giving Perry the instructions on the Supplemental Information screen, click OK. Perry's appointment now appears on the schedule.

12. Now that the appointment is booked, click Clear at the top right side of the screen to be prepared to book another appointment.

⊚ PUTTING IT ALL TOGETHER
TASK 2-4: SCHEDULING APPOINTMENTS

This task requires you to schedule appointments for the following patients without using step-by-step instructions as given in the previous tasks. *Remember to click OK through any collections alerts or other reminder notes in e-Medsys® for the purposes of these exercises.*

1. Screenings:

   A. Dr. Appolo has asked Harold Katt to make an appointment to check his cholesterol levels. Schedule a return office visit appointment for Harold on October 15, 2008, at 3:30 p.m.
   B. Ashley Mansfield, a patient of Dr. Medusa, is a diabetic and must be seen periodically to have her glucose levels checked. Schedule a return office visit appointment for Ashley for October 22, 2008 at 11:00 a.m.
   C. Donald Barr, a patient of Dr. Venus, is coming in to have his cholesterol levels checked. Schedule an appointment for October 23, 2008 at 9:30 a.m.

2. Candice Jones, a patient of Dr. Appolo, has been having some back pain related to an injury two weeks ago. Any time on the next available Wednesday, which is November 5, 2008, would be fine with her as that is her day off from work. Schedule an appointment (type: return office visit) for Candice on November 5, 2008 at 9:30 a.m.

3. Wilma Flint, a patient of Dr. Appolo, has been experiencing menopausal symptoms for the past several months. Schedule a follow-up visit for October 22, 2008, at 3:30 p.m.

4. Delores Bartel, a patient of Dr. Appolo, has a cough that has lingered for over a week. Schedule an appointment (return office visit) for October 23, 2008, at 3:00 p.m. at the Malibu office. (*Note:* "GASTMA" is the abbreviation for the Malibu office on the appointment schedule.)

5. Annual exams are a common reason for patient visits. Schedule annual exams for:

   A. Lacy Chickory, a patient of Dr. Appolo, on October 7, 2008, at 1:30 p.m. Ms. Chickory will be seen at the Malibu office.
   B. Perry Marshall, a patient of Dr. Venus, on October 16, 2008, at 2:00 p.m.
   C. Fred Willy, a patient of Dr. Appolo, on November 12, 2008, at 9:30 a.m.
   D. Garfield Poindexter, a patient of Dr. Zues, on November 18, 2008, at 9:00 a.m. Mr. Poindexter will be seen at the Malibu office.

6. Bruce Sawtell, a patient of Dr. Appolo, needs to schedule an appointment for November 14, 2008, at 11:30 a.m. for gastroenteritis.

7. Cory Haines, a patient of Dr. Zues, has a tick bite on his lower leg. Schedule an appointment for November 17, 2008, at 3:00 p.m. in the Malibu office.

8. Julie McMurrey, a patient of Dr. Venus, on October 7, 2008, at 9:30 a.m. She would like to discuss with Dr. Venus her recent unexplained weight loss.

9. Jodie Miller makes an appointment for an injection for her rheumatoid arthritis, which was ordered by Dr. Zues. Schedule a follow-up appointment for Jodie on October 28, 2008, at 10:00 a.m. in the Malibu office. (*Note:* When scheduling follow-up appointments, click Yes through any pop ups indicating Search Criteria do not match. This will allow you to continue booking the appointment.)

10. Crystal Nowell, a patient of Dr. Appolo, needs an appointment for a B-12 shot, which was ordered by Dr. Appolo. Schedule a follow-up appointment for Crystal on October 29, 2008, at 11:30 a.m.

11. Burt Ringer needs to make an appointment to receive a tetanus shot, which was ordered by Dr. Appolo. Schedule a follow-up appointment for Burt on November 11, 2008, at 3:00 p.m. in the Malibu office.

12. Curtis Russell, a patient of Dr. Zues, is experiencing recurring migraines. He has run out of his prescription of Duradrin and would like to schedule an appointment with Dr. Zues. Any time on the next available Monday would be fine with him, as that is his day off from work. Schedule a returning office visit for Curtis on November 10, 2008, at 2:00 p.m. in the Malibu office.

13. Reggie Williams, a new patient of Dr. Appolo, has been experiencing some bloating and abdominal pain for the past few weeks. He would prefer a late day appointment due to his hectic work schedule. Schedule a new patient appointment for Reggie on Thursday, November 6, 2008, at 3:30 p.m. in the Malibu office.

TASK 2-5: CANCELING AND RESCHEDULING AN APPOINTMENT

Today is November 10, 2008. Perry Marshall, patient of Dr. Venus, has a history of diverticulosis and after his last visit he was instructed to make an appointment for a sigmoidoscopy. Before leaving the office, he scheduled an appointment for Monday, November 17, 2008. Because he did not have his calendar with him at the time he made the appointment, once back in his office, he discovered that he was giving a presentation at his monthly sales meeting at that time. Perry contacts Dr. Venus's office to cancel the appointment and reschedule his procedure at a later date. The new appointment date is Tuesday, November 25, 2008, at 9:30 a.m.

1. Log in to e-Medsys®, if not already logged in. At the top of the screen, click on Scheduling. Click on Bookings from the drop-down box.

2. Search for Perry Marshall (in the Name field, enter Marshall, Perry and click Search). Click OK through the Collections Alert in the system. Now, Perry Marshall's appointment history appears on the Patient Appointment Information screen.

3. In the center of the screen, highlight Perry's appointment for November 17, 2008, then click Cancel.

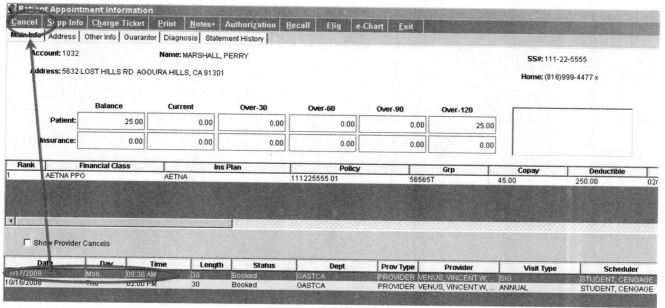

Reprinted with permission of TriMed Technologies, Corp.

4. In the Reason for Cancellation field, type "PATIENT NEEDS DIFFERENT DATE" and click the Patient Cancel button.

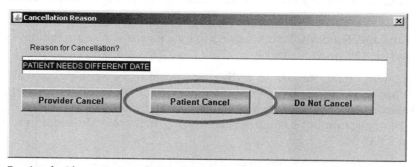

Reprinted with permission of TriMed Technologies, Corp.

5. Click Yes at the prompt for "Do You Wish to Reschedule this Appointment?"

6. This brings you to the main scheduling calendar screen. Select Perry's provider, Dr. Vincent Venus if not already selected (*Hint:* click on the Provider button, select Dr. Venus and click OK).

7. Using the calendar icon, select November 25, 2008, the date that Perry wishes to reschedule the appointment.

8. Be sure the Visit Type drop-down is Sig. Click on the 9:30 a.m. appointment row to highlight the slot.

9. Click Book.

10. Click Roll Up Slots at the prompt, since the provider has indicated that "Any" appointment may be booked at this time.

11. Now the rescheduled appointment appears on the calendar.

TIME	Mon (11/24/08) (0 Appts)	Tue (11/25/08) (1 Appts)	Wed (11/26/08) (0 Appts)
07:00 AM			
07:15 AM			
07:30 AM	GASTCA OUT	GASTCA OUT	GASTCA OUT
07:45 AM	GASTCA OUT	GASTCA OUT	GASTCA OUT
08:00 AM	GASTCA OUT	GASTCA OUT	GASTCA OUT
08:15 AM	GASTCA OUT	GASTCA OUT	GASTCA OUT
08:30 AM	GASTCA OUT	GASTCA OUT	GASTCA OUT
08:45 AM	GASTCA OUT	GASTCA OUT	GASTCA OUT
09:00 AM	GASTCA EXT OV	GASTCA EXT OV	GASTCA EXT OV
09:15 AM			
09:30 AM	GASTCA ANY	MARSHALL, PERRY SIG	GASTCA ANY
09:45 AM	GASTCA ANY		GASTCA ANY
10:00 AM	GASTCA EXT OV	GASTCA EXT OV	GASTCA EXT OV
10:15 AM			
10:30 AM	GASTCA ANY	GASTCA ANY	GASTCA ANY
10:45 AM	GASTCA ANY	GASTCA ANY	GASTCA ANY
11:00 AM	GASTCA EXT OV	GASTCA EXT OV	GASTCA EXT OV
11:15 AM			
11:30 AM	GASTCA OUT	GASTCA OUT	GASTCA OUT
11:45 AM	GASTCA OUT	GASTCA OUT	GASTCA OUT
12:00 PM	GASTCA OUT	GASTCA OUT	GASTCA OUT

Reprinted with permission of TriMed Technologies, Corp.

12. Now that the appointment is booked, click Clear at the top right side of the screen to be prepared to book another appointment.

 # PUTTING IT ALL TOGETHER

TASK 2-6: CANCELING AND RESCHEDULING APPOINTMENTS

This task requires you to cancel and reschedule appointments for the following patients without using step-by-step instructions as given in the previous tasks.

1. Ashley Mansfield, patient of Dr. Medusa, is a diabetic and must be seen periodically to have her glucose levels checked. She had made an appointment for October 22, 2008, at 11:00 a.m. but realized after booking the appointment that she has a previously scheduled dental appointment at that same time. Ashley would like to reschedule her appointment to another day during that week. Schedule the new appointment for October 30, 2008, at 11:15 a.m.

2. Wilma Flint, a patient of Dr. Appolo, has been experiencing menopausal symptoms for the past several months. She previously scheduled her follow-up visit for October 22, 2008, at 3:30 p.m. but realized her grandson has a baseball game at that time. She calls the office to cancel that appointment and reschedule for Monday, October 27, 2008, at the same time.

Patient Authorizations

In this module, you will:

1. Enter data to request a patient authorization from an insurance company.

2. Track the authorization through to Approved status.

TASK 3-1: REQUESTING A PATIENT AUTHORIZATION

Today is October 10, 2008. Marge Demo is a patient of Dr. Medusa. She is being treated for abdominal pain. Dr. Medusa refers her to Dr. Appolo for an office consultation.

You call Mutual of Omaha (phone number 818-596-6020) today to request this authorization, and speak with Sarah Smith. The insurance company's fax number is 818-596-6833.

1. Log in to e-Medsys®.

2. At the top of the screen, click on Billing.

3. Click on Inquiry from the drop-down box. (You can also get to this screen by pressing Ctrl + I [the shortcut command] on the keyboard.)

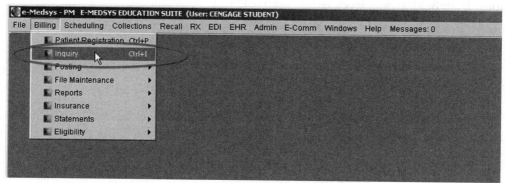

Reprinted with permission of TriMed Technologies, Corp.

47

4. An Inquiry screen appears.

5. Search for Marge Demo by typing DEMO in the Name field, and clicking the Search button.

6. Highlight Marge Demo's name on the Patient Search screen and click OK. (This screen appears when there is more than one patient who fits the search criteria. If there is only one patient who fits the search criteria, the program automatically brings the patient's account on the Patient Registration screen without this step.)

7. Marge has a Collections Alert in the system, which will appear as a pop-up. Click OK.

> **Note:** The e-Medsys® program includes built-in reminders, such as this one. For the purposes of these exercises, we will click through the system reminders.

8. Now Marge's information appears in the Inquiry screen.

9. At the top of the screen, click the Authorization button.

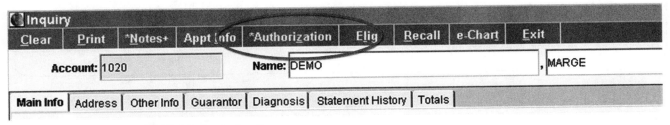

10. The Patient Authorization File Maintenance screen appears. Click the Add button.

11. A new screen appears. In the Type field, select Referral In from the drop-down list, since Dr. Appolo works in the same practice. (Referral Out would be used to refer a patient to another facility.)

12. In the Status field, select Requested from the drop-down list.

13. In the Request Date field, type today's date, 10/10/2008.

14. In the Primary Care Provider field, type MED—the first few letters of Dr. Medusa's last name.

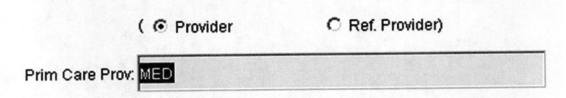

15. Press the Enter key on your keyboard. Dr. Medusa's name is now populated in this field.

16. In the Specialty Provider field, type APPO (to search for Dr. Appolo), and press Enter on the keyboard. Dr. Appolo's name is now populated in this field.

17. In the Diagnosis field, type % and press Enter on your keyboard to search for the diagnosis code. Searching using the "%" symbol searches for all diagnosis codes in the system.

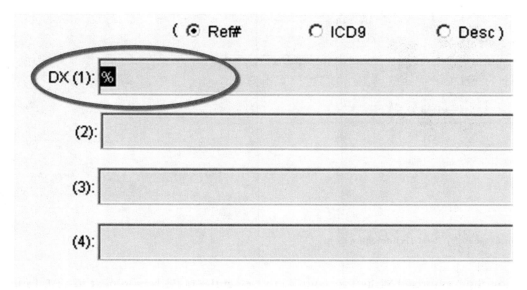

Reprinted with permission of TriMed Technologies, Corp.

18. Select **ABDOMINAL PAIN UNSPEC SITE** and click **OK**.

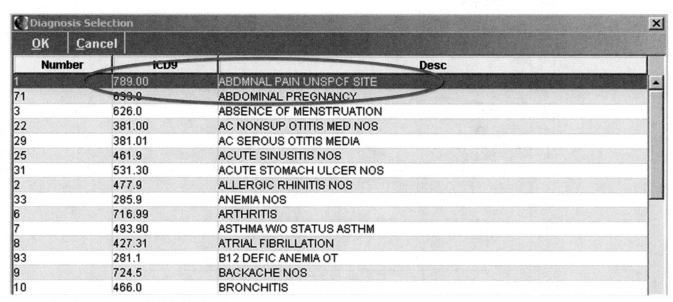

Reprinted with permission of TriMed Technologies, Corp.

19. Type the contact person's name (Smith, Sarah), phone number (818-596-6020), and fax number (818-596-6833). Check your work with the following screen shot, and click OK.

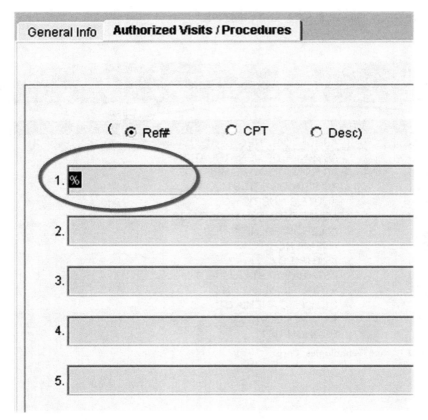

Reprinted with permission of TriMed Technologies, Corp.

20. Now click on the Authorized Visits/Procedures tab. Select the radio button next to CPT. In field 1, type % and press the Enter key on your keyboard to search and select the appropriate procedure code.

Reprinted with permission of TriMed Technologies, Corp.

21. Find CPT 99243 "Office Consultation" and click OK. Now Office Consultation is populated in field 1. Type 1 in the Qty column. Check your work with this screen.

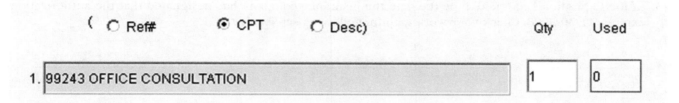

Reprinted with permission of TriMed Technologies, Corp.

22. Click the Accept button. Click OK on the Patient Authorization pop-up that tells you the authorization has been added.

23. Click Exit to get out of the Authorizations screen. Click the Clear button to get out of the patient's account. To exit the Inquiry screen and return to the main menu, click Exit again.

TASK 3-2: UPDATING A PATIENT AUTHORIZATION

Today is October 20, 2008. Mutual of Omaha has approved the Patient Authorization request (from October 10, 2008) for an office consultation for Marge Demo, a patient of Dr. Medusa. The authorization number is AP13579, and the authorization is valid until November 30, 2008.

1. Log in to e-Medsys®.

2. At the top of the screen, click on Billing.

3. Click on Inquiry from the drop-down box. (You can also get to this screen by pressing Ctrl + I (the shortcut command) on the keyboard.)

4. An Inquiry Screen appears. Search for Marge Demo by typing DEMO in the Name field, and clicking the Search button.

5. Highlight Marge Demo's name on the Patient Search screen and click OK. (This screen appears when there is more than one patient who fits the search criteria. If there is only one patient who fits the search criteria, the program automatically brings the patient's account on the Patient Registration screen without this step.)

6. Click OK through the Collections Alert pop-up.

7. Now Marge's information appears in the Inquiry screen.

8. At the top of the screen, click the Authorization button. The Patient Authorization File Maintenance screen appears.

9. Highlight the request from October 10, 2008, and click the Modify button.

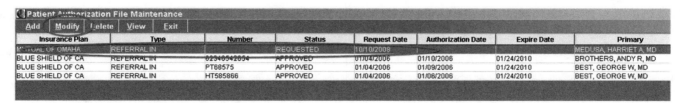

Reprinted with permission of TriMed Technologies, Corp.

10. Type the authorization number, AP13579, in the Auth Number field.

11. Use the drop-down menu to change the status to Approved.

12. Type today's date, 10/20/2008 in the Auth Date field.

13. In the Expiration Date field, type the date the insurance company has designated that the authorization expires, 11/30/2008. Check your work with the following screen shot.

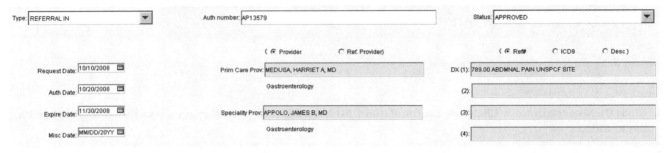

Reprinted with permission of TriMed Technologies, Corp.

14. Click the Accept button.

15. Click Exit on the Patient Authorization File Maintenance screen. Click the Clear button to get out of the patient's account. To exit the Inquiry screen and return to the main menu, click Exit again.

⦿ PUTTING IT ALL TOGETHER
TASK 3-3: PATIENT AUTHORIZATIONS

This task requires you to track an authorization for patient Pat Bright without using step-by-step instructions as given in the previous task. Today is October 13, 2008.

1. Pat Bright, a patient of Dr. Zues, is experiencing some problems with rapid heartbeat and has an appointment with Dr. Zues to express her concerns. After examining Pat and discussing her symptoms, Dr. Zues would like her to make an office consultation appointment (CPT 99243) with Dr. Sue Apple for cardiac dysrhythmia.

2. Insurance company contact information: Rhonda Ramirez; phone 781-681-9300; fax 781-681-9322.

3. Medicare approves the authorization on November 3, 2008. Authorization #: CD9987, expiring December 15, 2008.

Patient Reception

In this module, you will:

1. Mark on the schedule the arrival, registration, and admittance for patient appointments.

2. Update Patient Registration information when a patient checks in.

3. Produce a printed charge ticket that enables the provider to mark service(s) performed during a patient appointment.

TASK 4-1: CHECKING IN PATIENTS UPON ARRIVAL— REGISTRATION UPDATES

Today is November 10, 2008. Curtis Russell, a patient of Dr. Zues, is experiencing recurring migraines. He has run out of his prescription of Duradrin and has scheduled an appointment with Dr. Zues. He currently has an insurance plan called Motion Picture Industry through Blue Cross. The plan has recently been expanded, and there have been some minor changes:

- The Group Number will change to GR7676700.

- The Policy Number will change to 46655997RN.

- The Co-payment amount will increase to $30.00.

- The effective date of the plan changes is 10/01/2008.

He arrives at the medical office 15 minutes before his appointment time. During check in, you will need to make these changes to Curtis's registration information.

1. Log in to e-Medsys®.

2. At the top of the screen, click on Scheduling. Click on Bookings from the drop-down box or press Ctrl + B on the keyboard. The Appointment Scheduling screen will now appear.

3. Click on Calendar button, and use the arrows to find today's date.

4. Now click on the Provider button that appears in the left-hand corner of the screen. Highlight Dr. Zues, to bring up his schedule for the day. Click OK.

5. Now find Curtis's appointment on the schedule. Right click on the appointment slot.

6. Roll the mouse over the patient's name, RUSSELL, CURTIS ▶ and select Arrived.

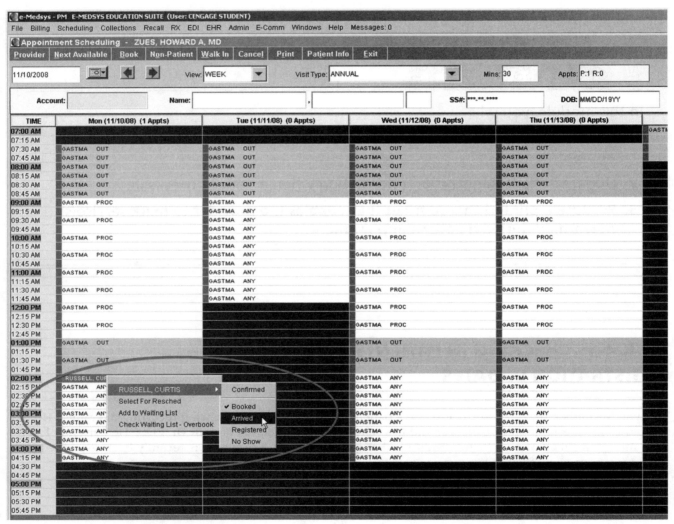

Reprinted with permission of TriMed Technologies, Corp.

7. Click OK through the collections alert in the system. The Patient Appointment Information screen is now shown. This is a snapshot of the patient's account and can be used to confirm whether registration updates need to be made. You confirm that this patient does have updates.

8. At the top of the screen, click on Billing. Click on Patient Registration from the drop-down box.

9. The Patient Registration screen will appear. Search for Curtis Russell's account, by typing Russell in the last name field, and clicking the Search button.

10. Curtis's information appears in the Patient Registration screen. Click on the Insurance tab.

11. The patient's insurance information is displayed in the top table. Click on the row, Blue Cross, Motion Picture Industry, to select the insurance to be modified.

12. Click on the Modify Ins button on the right side of the screen.

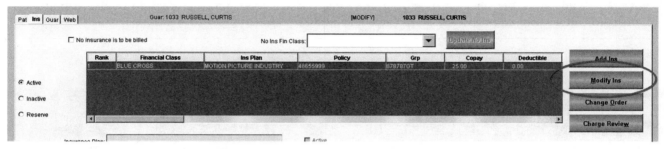

Reprinted with permission of TriMed Technologies, Corp.

13. Now, the bottom of the screen is populated with the plan detail information.

14. Update the following fields, and check your work with the following screen shot.

- In the Effective Date field, type 10/01/2008.
- In the Group Number field, type GR7676700.
- In the Policy Number field, type 46655997RN.
- In the co-pay field, type $30.00.

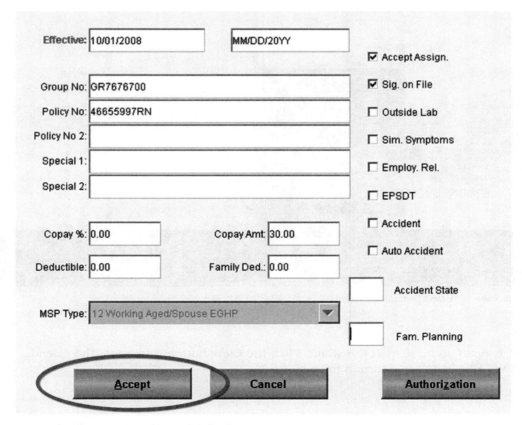

Reprinted with permission of TriMed Technologies, Corp.

15. Click the Accept button to save the changes. Click Yes through the prompt.

16. Click Clear to exit out of Curtis's account, and then click Exit to exit out of the patient registration area. You are back on the Patient Appointment Information screen. Click Exit on this screen to return to the Appointment Scheduling calendar.

17. Now, right click Curtis's appointment slot and roll the mouse over to the second drop-down and select Registered, as you have already updated his information. The program adds a time stamp after Registered.

> **Note:** Once Registered is selected, the program adds a new category to the drop-down list: Admitted. (This is for informational purposes; do not select Admitted at this point.)

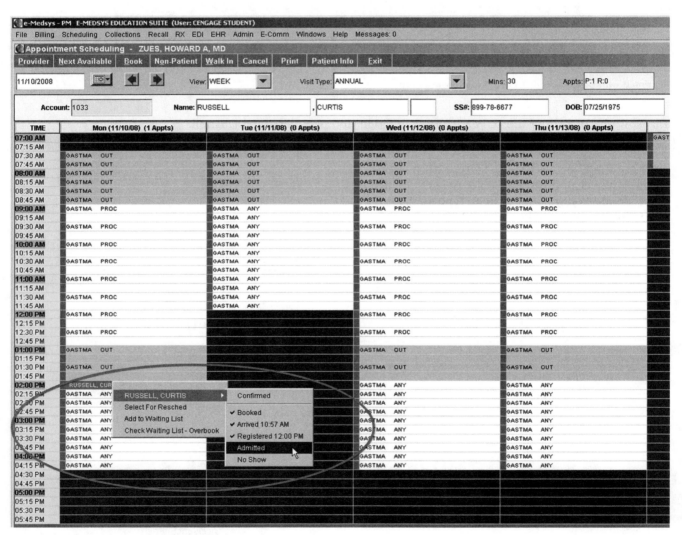

Reprinted with permission of TriMed Technologies, Corp.

18. The patient is ready to be seen at this point. Click the Clear button to prepare the calendar for the next entry. Click the Exit button to return to the main menu.

TASK 4-2: CHECKING IN PATIENTS UPON ARRIVAL— NO REGISTRATION UPDATES

Today is October 16, 2008. Elizabeth Greenley, a new patient of Dr. Medusa, has arrived at the medical office at 10 a.m. for her appointment; an annual exam. You go over Elizabeth's registration information and insurance information with her, and find there are no updates to be made.

1. Log in to e-Medsys®.

2. At the top of the screen, click on Scheduling. Click on Bookings from the drop-down box or press Ctrl + B on the keyboard. The Appointment Scheduling screen will now appear.

3. Click on Calendar button, and use the arrows to find the correct month (October 2008) and then select the date, October 16.

4. Now click on the Provider button that appears in the left-hand corner of the screen. Highlight Dr. Medusa and click OK, to bring up Dr. Medusa's schedule on this day.

5. Now find Elizabeth's appointment, at 10:15 a.m., and right click on the appointment slot. Roll the mouse over GREENLEY, ELIZABETH ▶ and select Registered from the second drop-down menu.

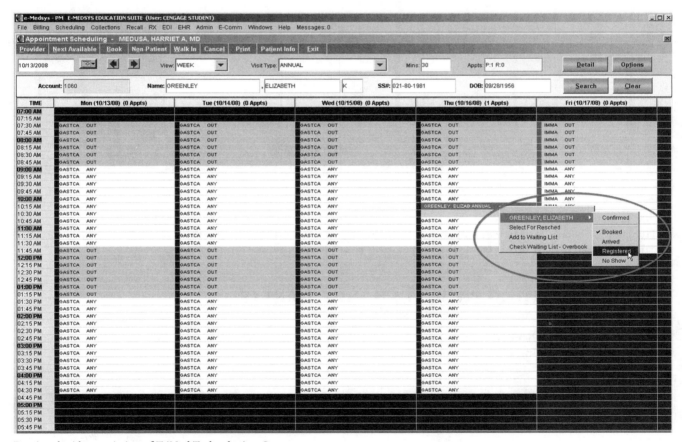

Reprinted with permission of TriMed Technologies, Corp.

6. The program brings up Elizabeth's Patient Appointment Information. This screen is a snapshot of the patient's account and can be used to confirm whether registration changes need to be made. There are no updates needed for this patient, so click Exit to return to the schedule.

7. The program automatically checks Arrived and Registered with the same time stamp.

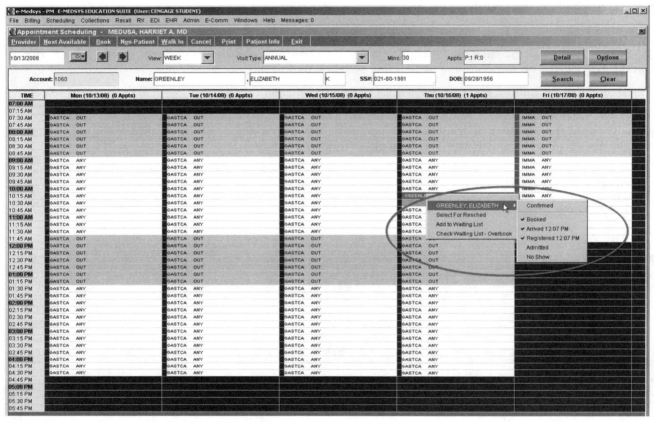

Reprinted with permission of TriMed Technologies, Corp.

8. The patient is ready to be seen at this point. When you have finished, click the Clear button to prepare the calendar for the next entry. Click the Exit button to return to the main menu.

TASK 4-3: PRINTING PATIENT CHARGE TICKETS

Now that Elizabeth is checked in, print a charge ticket for her appointment. This allows the provider to mark services performed during a patient appointment.

> **Note:** In a medical office with a total practice management system (both front-office functions and back office electronic charting capabilities), printing charge tickets may not be required, as charges will automatically be entered into the system during the provider's examination. This exercise is included to instruct in the instance that an office has a practice management system (for front office tasks) and still uses paper charts.

1. Log in to e-Medsys®.

2. At the top of the screen, click on Scheduling.

3. Click on Bookings from the drop-down box or press Ctrl + B on the keyboard. The Appointment Scheduling screen will now appear.

4. Search for Elizabeth Greenley, by typing Greenley, Elizabeth in the Name field, and click the Search button.

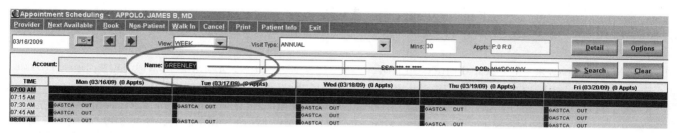

Reprinted with permission of TriMed Technologies, Corp.

5. This action brings up Patient Appointment Information for Elizabeth.

6. Be sure that the 10/16/2008 appointment for Elizabeth is highlighted in the center of the screen, and click the Charge Ticket button.

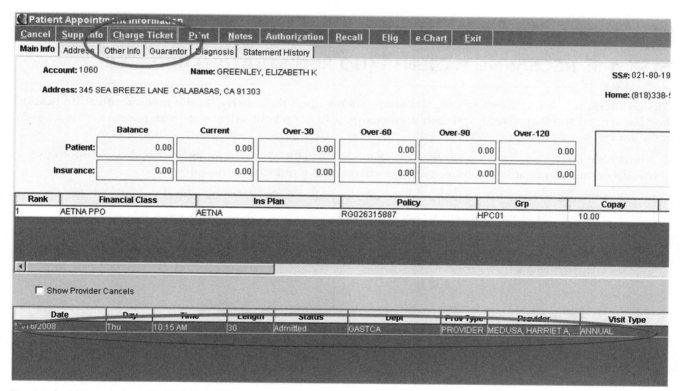

Reprinted with permission of TriMed Technologies, Corp.

7. The charge ticket will print to your local printer. Label the charge ticket Task 4-3.

8. Click Exit when you are finished, and close the Scheduling area and return to the main menu when you are finished.

PUTTING IT ALL TOGETHER

TASK 4-4: RECEIVING PATIENTS (WITH REGISTRATION UPDATES)

This task requires you to check in a patient (indicating Arrived on the schedule) and update registration information (then, indicating Registered on the schedule) without using step-by-step instructions as given in the previous tasks.

1. Fred Willy arrives at the medical office on November 11, 2008, for his appointment with Dr. Appolo. He currently has an Aetna PPO plan. There will now be a $10 co-payment and a deductible of $250.

2. Ashley Mansfield arrives at the medical office on October 30, 2008, for her glucose screening appointment with Dr. Medusa. She informs you that she has a new home phone number, 805-327-5588. She would also like to add her mother, Joyce Mansfield, as an emergency contact. Mrs. Manfield's phone number is 805-788-3443.

3. Perry Marshall arrives at the medical office on November 25, 2008, for his sigmoidoscopy appointment with Dr. Venus per previous tasks. Add his brother as Perry's emergency contact to his registration: James Marshall, 818-555-9631.

 # PUTTING IT ALL TOGETHER

TASK 4-5: RECEIVING PATIENTS (NO REGISTRATION UPDATES)

This task requires you to check in the following patients upon their arrival to the medical office (indicating they are Arrived and Registered), and then print charge tickets, without using step-by-step instructions as given in the previous tasks.

1. Wilma Flint arrives at the medical office on October 27, 2008, for her appointment with Dr. Appolo to follow-up on her menopausal symptoms. Print a charge ticket and label it Task 4-5A.

2. Reggie Williams arrives at the medical office on November 6, 2008, for his appointment with Dr. Appolo. Print a charge ticket and label it Task 4-5B.

Working in the Patient Electronic Medical Record

OBJECTIVES

In this module, you will:

1. Use the appointment schedule on the EHR side of the program, indicating patients have been admitted to an exam room.

2. Create new patient notes in an electronic patient record.

3. Enter patient history information into the patient record.

4. Enter vital signs information into the patient record.

5. Record Review of Systems (ROS) information from a patient questionnaire for provider review.

6. Record past history, family history, social history in the patient record for provider review.

TASK 5-1: ADMITTING PATIENTS USING THE EHR SCHEDULE

Today is October 16, 2008.

You are working with Dr. Venus today as a clinical medical assistant. Perry Marshall, a patient of Dr. Venus, arrives for his annual exam. He completes an ROS form while in the waiting area, and the administrative medical assistant confirms that there are no registration updates at this time. Once Perry has been brought into the exam room, you will change his appointment status to Admitted.

1. Log in to e-Medsys®.

2. Using the steps learned in Module 4, indicate on the appointment schedule that Perry has Arrived and Registered.

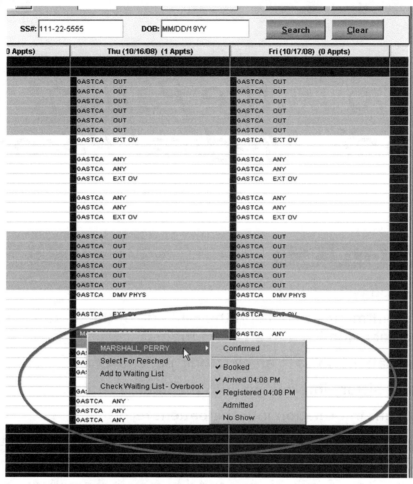

Reprinted with permission of TriMed Technologies, Corp.

3. At the top of the screen, click on EHR, and then click on EHR Home Page from the drop-down box.

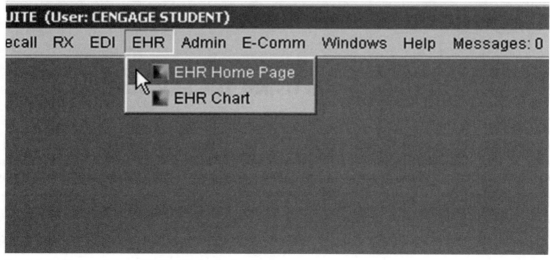

Reprinted with permission of TriMed Technologies, Corp.

4. This opens the EHR page in a new window.

5. Now, you will open Dr. Venus's schedule—in the EHR side of the program

- On the right side of the screen, select Dr. Venus from the list of providers.
- Type in 10/16/2008 and press the TAB button on your keyboard to find the correct date.
- Below the calendar, be sure the radio buttons next to Cal and Daily are selected (this indicates that you want to view the Calendar for only today's date).

Reprinted with permission of TriMed Technologies, Corp.

6. Dr. Venus's schedule appears in the center of the page. You will see Perry Marshall's appointment on the schedule.

7. Now, right click on Perry Marshall's name on the schedule.

8. Roll your mouse over Status ► and then click on Admitted. This provides a timestamp for when the patient was admitted to an exam room.

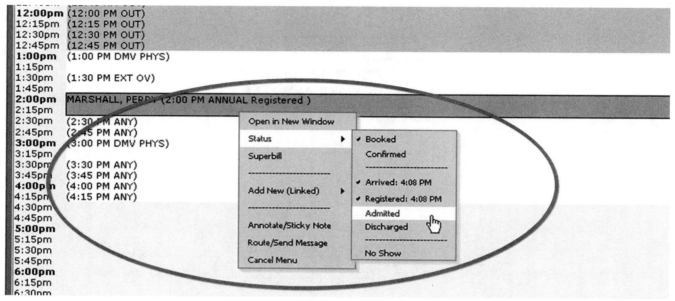

Reprinted with permission of TriMed Technologies, Corp.

TASK 5-2: LINKING A NEW ANNUAL EXAM NOTE TO A PATIENT APPOINTMENT AND ENTERING PATIENT DATA

Now that you have indicated Perry Marshall has been admitted to an exam room, you will create a new patient note in his patient record.

1. While still on Dr. Venus's schedule, right click on Perry Marshall's name again.

2. This time, select Add New (Linked) ► and then click on Patient Note from the menu.

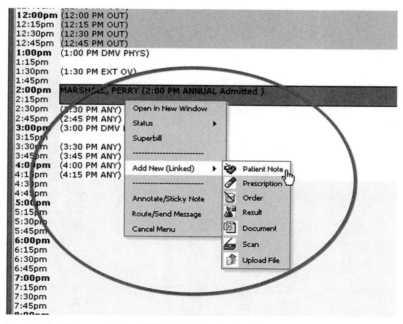

Reprinted with permission of TriMed Technologies, Corp.

3. Now you are in the patient's individual chart, and a New Note has opened on the bottom right side of the screen. You can click on the Box on the right side of the screen above the envelope icon (as shown in the following screen shot) to enlarge the New Note while you are working in it.

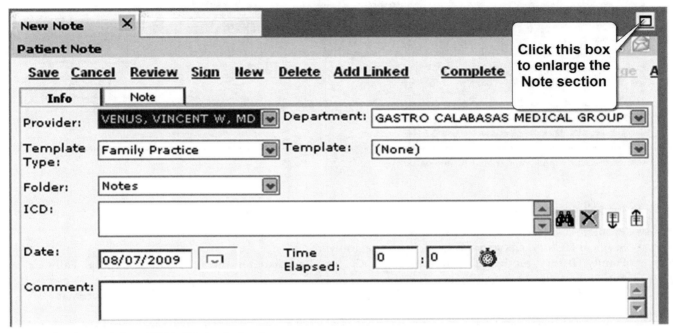

Reprinted with permission of TriMed Technologies, Corp.

4. In the Template field, use the drop-down to select Routine Exam Male. In the date field, enter 10/16/2008. (In a medical office setting, the date would be autopopulated based on today's date.)

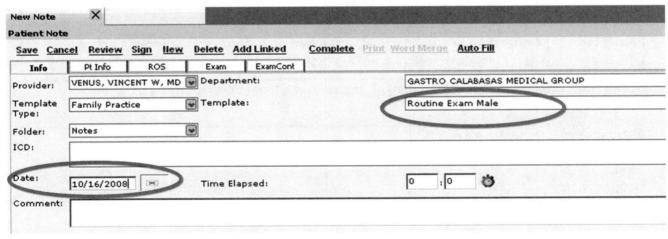

Reprinted with permission of TriMed Technologies, Corp.

5. Click Save.

6. Select the Pt Info tab.

7. Change the Date of Visit to 10/16/2008.

8. Click on the plus sign (+) next to Chief Complaint. This action will bring up a script, which lets you add additional drop-down items to the chief complaint list. Type in Annual Physical Exam and then click OK.

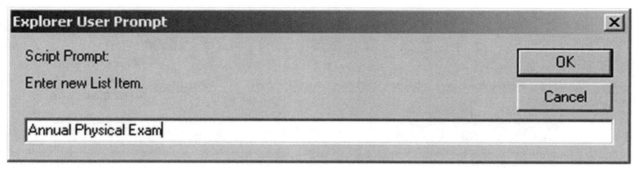

Reprinted with permission of TriMed Technologies, Corp.

9. In the following fields PMH (patient medical history), enter the following:

- Problem List: Arthritis; hypertension
- Surgical History: Cholecystectomy; appendectomy
- Family History: Mother died at age 70 of CAD, also had diabetes and rheumatoid arthritis; Father alive and well at age 74; no siblings
- Social History: Nonsmoker, social drinker, married with four children, works as a longshoreman

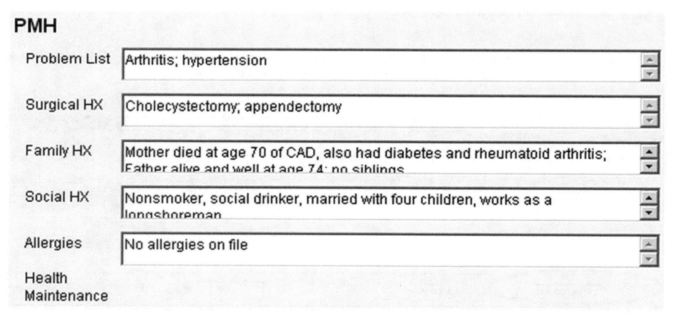

Reprinted with permission of TriMed Technologies, Corp.

10. Leave the rest of the screen for the provider to fill out. Click Save when you are finished.

TASK 5-3: ENTERING ROS INFORMATION FROM PATIENT QUESTIONNAIRE

Recall that in the waiting area, Perry completed a Patient Questionnaire to update the provider on his state of health. The medical assistant will enter the information into the patient's chart. All of this information will be reviewed with the patient and signed by Dr. Venus.

1. Still in the Perry Marshall's new Note, select the ROS tab. Note that the default settings are "normal," which helps save time when working in the chart. The person documenting needs to enter only remarkable or abnormal items.

2. In the first entry, Constitutional, keep the radio button set to normal, but in the free text section beneath, type Normal, slight weight loss.

Patient Note

| Save | Cancel | Review | Sign | New | Delete | Add Linked | Complete | Print | Word Merge | Auto Fill |

| Info | Pt Info | ROS | Exam | ExamCont |

Constitutional   ⦿ Normal   ○ Abnormal   ○ Didn't Ask

    Normal, slight weight loss

Reprinted with permission of TriMed Technologies, Corp.

3. Now enter the following information for the MS (musculoskeletal), GI (gastrointestinal), and GV (genitourinary) systems:

   • GI: Abnormal; Experiencing intermittent bouts of diarrhea and constipation
   • GV: Abnormal; Frequent urination during the night
   • MS: Abnormal; Joint pain in fingers and elbows

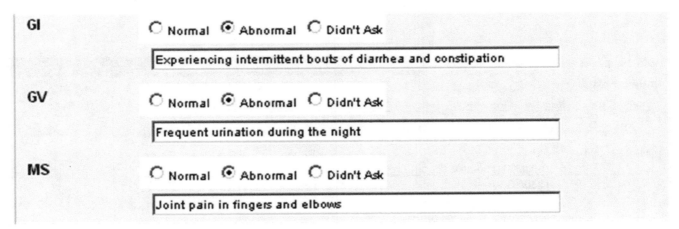

GI   ○ Normal   ⦿ Abnormal   ○ Didn't Ask

    Experiencing intermittent bouts of diarrhea and constipation

GV   ○ Normal   ⦿ Abnormal   ○ Didn't Ask

    Frequent urination during the night

MS   ○ Normal   ⦿ Abnormal   ○ Didn't Ask

    Joint pain in fingers and elbows

Reprinted with permission of TriMed Technologies, Corp.

4. Click Save when you are finished.

TASK 5-4: ENTERING PATIENT VITAL SIGNS ON A PATIENT NOTE

After taking the patient's vital signs, enter them into the new Note.

1. Still in Perry Marshall's chart, select the Exam tab.

2. Enter the following information in the appropriate fields:

   - Height: 73 inches
   - Weight: 210 pounds
   - Blood Pressure (sitting): 120/65
   - Pulse: 67
   - Respiration: 17
   - Temperature: 98.6°F

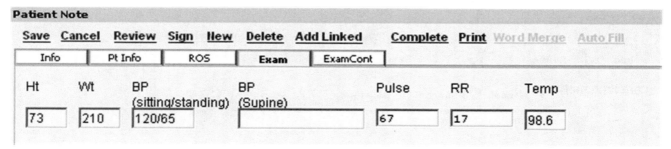

Reprinted with permission of TriMed Technologies, Corp.

3. Click Save when you are finished. The provider will complete the rest of this page during the exam.

4. Now click the Print button, and select PDF Form. Print to your local printer, and label the printout as Task 5-4.

5. When you are done, minimize the right side of the screen by clicking on the same Box on the right of the screen, above the envelope icon.

6. Then, click the X on the Routine Exam tab.

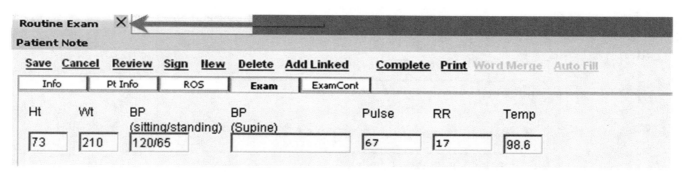

Reprinted with permission of TriMed Technologies, Corp.

TASK 5-5: NAVIGATING THE PATIENT CHART USING TREE VIEW

This exercise is designed to familiarize you with the navigation of individual patient charts. You should still be in Perry Marshall's chart.

1. So far, you have learned how to enter information in one area of the chart (creating a new Note). On the lower left side of the screen, you should see a group of vertical tabs. This is your "left navigation" bar.

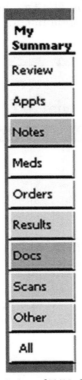

Reprinted with permission of TriMed Technologies, Corp.

2. Click on Appts. This will show all of the appointments that have been scheduled for Perry at the medical office. Make sure the box next to "Tree" is selected (the next step gives more explanation on Tree View). Make sure the box next to "Appts: Inc. Canc" is *not* selected. This suppresses appointments that were cancelled.

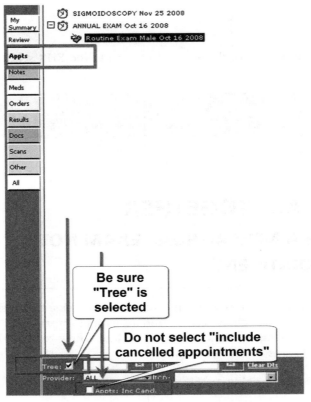

Reprinted with permission of TriMed Technologies, Corp.

3. Tree View shows items as they are connected with one another. So, on your screen, you should see that Perry Marshall has two appointments (one on November 25, and one on October 16). The October 16 appointment has a patient Note associated with it. The Tree View will continue to build when additional items are added to the patient's chart during each appointment.

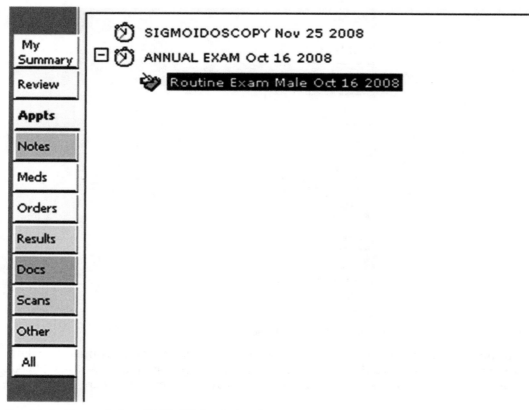

Reprinted with permission of TriMed Technologies, Corp.

4. Click on the Home button at the top of the screen to return to the EHR schedule.

Reprinted with permission of TriMed Technologies, Corp.

PUTTING IT ALL TOGETHER

TASK 5-6: LINKING A NEW ANNUAL EXAM NOTE TO A PATIENT APPOINTMENT

Without using step-by-step instructions as given in the previous tasks, this task requires you to (1) receive the patient (indicating Arrived on the schedule), (2) update patient information (indicating Registered on the schedule), (3) admit the patient using the EHR schedule, (4) link a new Note to the patient's appointment, and (5) enter information and vital signs in the new Note.

Garfield Poindexter arrives for his appointment on November 18, 2008. Using the following information, enter data in his chart prior to being seen for his annual exam with Dr. Zues. Upon check-in, Mr. Poindexter indicates that he has a new work phone number, (310) 558-2893 x112, and he now has a cell phone number, (779) 438-3388. He has also advised you that his emergency contact is Gayle Rafferty with a contact number of (779) 438-2397.

When you have finished entering the information in the patient's record, print your work and label it Task 5-6.

Chief Complaint	Annual Physical Exam (*hint:* this is now in the drop-down list)
Also here to discuss:	Sore shoulder for past two weeks, palpitations
Surgical History	Arthroscopic surgery on left knee
Family History	Mother alive and well; Father deceased one year ago at age 60 by massive heart attack; older brother with history of chronic asthma; younger brother healthy
Social History	Single, nonsmoker, social drinker, no illicit drug use, drinks five to eight cups of coffee per day
Constitutional	Healthy appearing, no significant weight fluctuations
Musculoskeletal	Pain in left shoulder, left ankle gives out sometimes
Neurological	Headaches (several per week)
Gastrointestinal	Frequent nausea without vomiting
Height	75 inches
Weight	237 pounds
Blood Pressure	118/70 (sitting)
Pulse	70
Respiration	19
Temperature	99.1

TASK 5-7: LINKING A NEW MULTISYSTEM EXAM NOTE TO A PATIENT APPOINTMENT AND ENTERING VITAL SIGNS

Today is October 23, 2008.

You are working with Dr. Appolo today. Delores Bartel is a patient of Dr. Appolo and is being seen today for a cough that has lingered for over a week. The patient does not have registration updates today.

1. Log in to e-Medsys®.

2. Using the steps learned in Module 4, indicate on the appointment schedule that the patient has arrived and is registered.

3. Click on EHR from the top menu, and then select EHR Home Page from the drop-down box. This opens the EHR Home Page in a new window.

4. Open Dr. Appolo's schedule on the EHR schedule, and navigate to today's date.

5. Find Delores's appointment, and indicate that she has been Admitted.

6. Using the EHR schedule, right click on the patient's appointment, and link a new Note to the appointment.

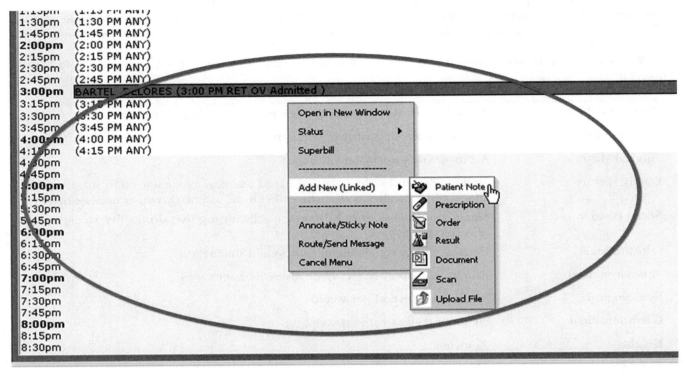

Reprinted with permission of TriMed Technologies, Corp.

7. Now the patient's individual chart appears on the screen, and the lower right side of the screen has a New Note. (Recall that you can enlarge the New Note while you are working in it.) In the Template field, use the drop-down to select MultisystemE&M1. Change the Date to 10/23/2008. Click Save.

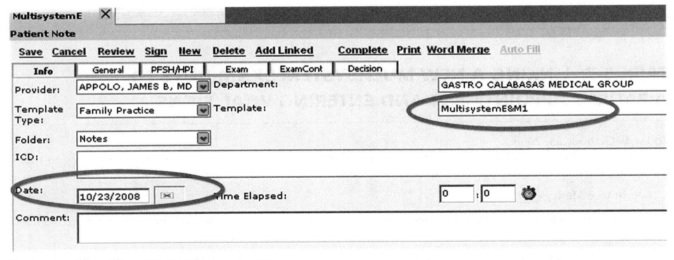

Reprinted with permission of TriMed Technologies, Corp.

8. Now, click on the General tab. Enter the following information:

- Height: 66 inches
- Weight: 148 pounds
- Blood Pressure: 117/67 (sitting)
- Pulse: 66
- Respiration: 25 (rapid and shallow)
- Temperature: 102°F
- General appearance: Ashen, lethargic
- CC: Has had a lingering cough for over a week

Patient Note

Save Cancel Review Sign New Delete Add Linked   Complete Print Word Merge Auto Fill

| Info | General | PFSH/HPI | Exam | ExamCont | Decision |

height: 66

weight: 148

BP:(sitting/standing)   117/67

BP:(Supine)

Pulse: 66

Respiration: 25 (rapid and shallo‹

Temperature: 102

General appearance   Ashen, lethargic

CC: Has had a lingering cough for over a week

Reprinted with permission of TriMed Technologies, Corp.

9. When you are finished entering this information, click Save.

TASK 5-8: ENTERING PATIENT, FAMILY, AND SOCIAL HISTORY (PFSH) ON A PATIENT NOTE

1. Still in the same note, click on the PFSH/HPI tab.

2. Click on the box with the three dots next to the Social History field and select "smokes" and "drinks." (Clicking anywhere outside of the drop-down box will return you to the PFSH screen.)

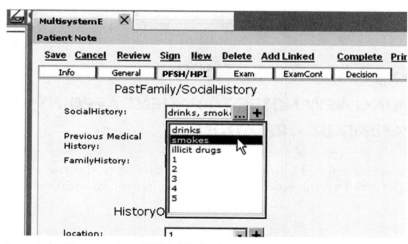

Reprinted with permission of TriMed Technologies, Corp.

3. Click on the plus sign next to Previous Medical History.

4. Enter Chronic bronchitis in the pop-up box and click OK.

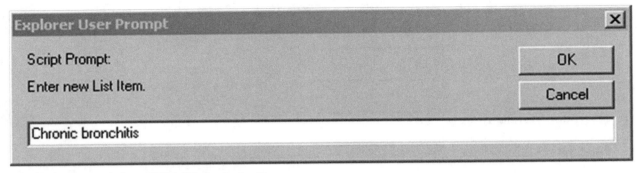

Reprinted with permission of TriMed Technologies, Corp.

5. Click on the plus sign next to Family History. Enter COPD in the pop-up box and click OK.

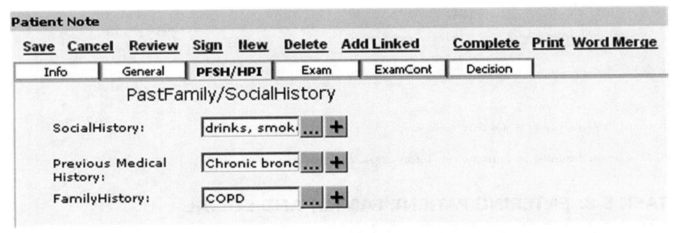

Reprinted with permission of TriMed Technologies, Corp.

6. Click Save when you have finished. The provider will complete the rest of this page during the exam.

7. Now click the Print button, and select PDF Form. Print to your local printer, and label the printout as Task 5-8.

8. When you are done, minimize the right side of the screen.

9. Then, click the X on the MultisystemE tab.

 # PUTTING IT ALL TOGETHER

TASK 5-9: LINKING NEW NOTES TO PATIENT APPOINTMENTS AND RECORDING PATIENT INFORMATION

Without using step-by-step instructions as given in the previous tasks, this task requires you to (1) receive the patient (indicating Arrived on the schedule), (2) update patient information if appropriate (indicating

Registered on the schedule), (3) admit the patient using the EHR schedule, (4) link a new Note to the patient's appointment, and (5) enter information and vital signs in the new Note.

1. Bruce Sawtelle arrives for his appointment on November 14, 2008. He has no updates to his registration information. Using the following information, create a multisystem exam template note for Bruce Sawtelle, who is being seen by Dr. Appolo for gastroenteritis. When you have finished entering the information in the patient's record, print your work and label it Task 5-9A.

Height	69 inches
Weight	186 pounds
Blood Pressure	120/72 (sitting)
Pulse	67
Respirations	16
Temperature	100.4°F
General Appearance	Slightly flushed, guarded
Social History	Married with two children, both healthy; nonsmoker, drinks two bottles of beer per day during the week and about one six-pack per day on weekends, sometimes accompanied by hard liquor
Previous Medical History	Chronic asthma
Family History	Mother alive—hypertension, diabetes, and ulcerative colitis; Father alive—prostate Ca, and hypercholesterolemia; younger sister healthy with no chronic conditions

2. Cory Haines arrives for his appointment on November 17, 2008. He has no updates to his registration information. Using the following information, create a new multisystem exam template for Cory Haines who is being seen by Dr. Zues for a tick bite on his lower leg. When you have finished entering the information in the patient's record, print your work and label it Task 5-9B.

Height	72 inches
Weight	198 pounds
Blood Pressure	117/67 (sitting)
Pulse	65
Respirations	17
Temperature	98.6°F
General Appearance	Healthy, in no acute distress
Social History	Single, nonsmoker, social drinker. Physically active, involved in hiking and working out at the gym. Employed as a surgical technician
Previous Medical History	Fractured tibia—right leg
Family History	Mother alive and healthy; Father alive and healthy; younger sister and two brothers all healthy with no chronic conditions

3. Julie McMurrey arrives for her appointment on October 7, 2008, to discuss her recent unexplained weight loss with Dr. Venus. Using the information in the following table, enter data in her chart prior to being seen for her annual exam with Dr. Venus. Additionally, when she checks into the office, she says she and her husband have moved to a new address: 439 Crandall Wood Drive, Simi Valley, CA 93065. All other information remains the same. She would like to add her husband, Brian Austin, as her emergency contact. His cell phone number is 805-312-6765. When you have finished entering the information in the patient's record, print your work and label it Task 5-7C.

Height	67 inches
Weight	106 pounds
Blood Pressure	117/68 (sitting)
Pulse	68
Respiration	18
Temperature	98.4°F
General Appearance	Healthy appearing
Social History	Married, three children all alive and healthy, nonsmoker, nondrinker, works in healthcare as an RN, no illicit drug use
Previous Medical History	T&A; appendectomy
Family History	Mother, uterine Ca at 55 TAH performed, hypertension; Father, chronic bronchitis due to smoking, hypertension, hypercholesterolemia; two sisters, both alive and healthy

Creating Prescriptions for Provider Authorization

OBJECTIVES

In this module, you will:

1. Enter prescription information indicated by the provider.

2. Send the prescription as a message to the provider to sign off and approve the prescription.

TASK 6-1: CREATING A PRESCRIPTION FOR LACY CHICKORY

Today is October 7, 2008.

Dr. Appolo has prescribed Lisinopril (20 mg), 30 tablets for Lacy Chickory, who has hypertension. He has indicated that she should take one each day for a month; the patient may have six refills.

1. Log in to e-Medsys®.

2. Using the steps learned in Module 4, indicate on the appointment schedule that Lacy has Arrived and Registered.

3. Then, open the EHR Home Page, and using the steps learned in Module 5, indicate on the EHR schedule that Lacy has been Admitted.

4. Now, double click on Lacy's appointment on the EHR schedule. This is a shortcut that brings you directly to Lacy's individual patient record. Your screen should look like the following screen shot.

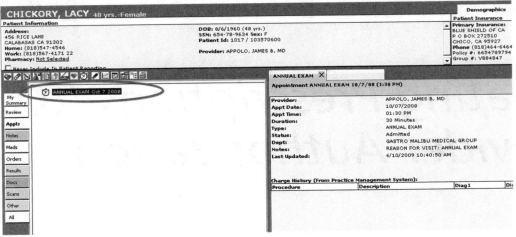

Reprinted with permission of TriMed Technologies, Corp.

Troubleshooting: Locating an Individual Patient Chart

1. Besides double clicking on a patient's appointment on the EHR schedule, you can also access individual patient charts by following these steps. From the menu along the top of the page, click on Chart.

Reprinted with permission of TriMed Technologies, Corp.

2. This action will bring up a search screen for finding a patient chart. You can either:

   A. Type in the patient's last name (in this case, Chickory) and click Enter on your keyboard (see the following screen shot); or

   B. Click the first letter of the patient's last name (C) along the left side of the screen. All patients with the last name of "C" will appear on your screen.

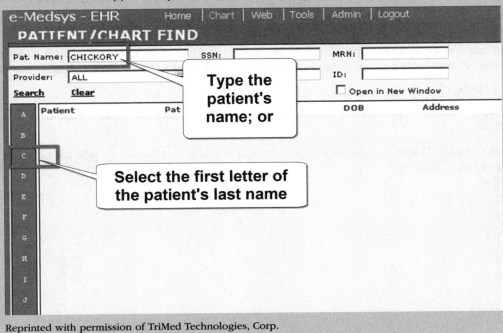

Reprinted with permission of TriMed Technologies, Corp.

3. Double click the patient's name to open the patient's chart.

4. Once in the patient's chart, on the left menu, click on Appts to prepare to link your new item to a patient appointment.

5. Right click on today's appointment.

6. This action brings up a menu similar to what you saw on the EHR schedule. Select Add New (Linked) ▶ and then click on Prescription.

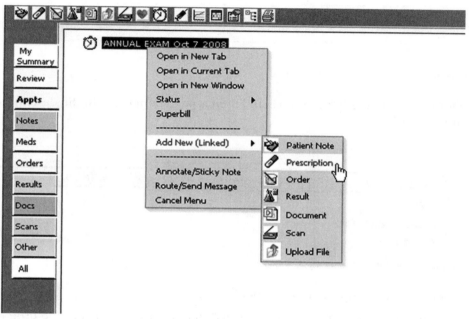

Reprinted with permission of TriMed Technologies, Corp.

7. When you select this, a new Prescription tab opens on the bottom right side of the screen. You can enlarge the tab by clicking on the corner box.

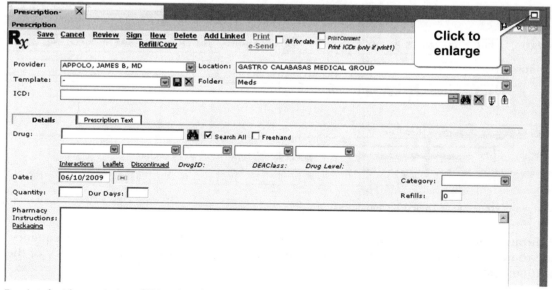

Reprinted with permission of TriMed Technologies, Corp.

8. Within this tab, the provider (Dr. Appolo) name and the location will autopopulate based on the patient selected. Leave the Template field blank. The Folder field is autopopulated with Meds.

9. To the right of the ICD field, click on the binoculars to search for the diagnosis related to the medication being prescribed.

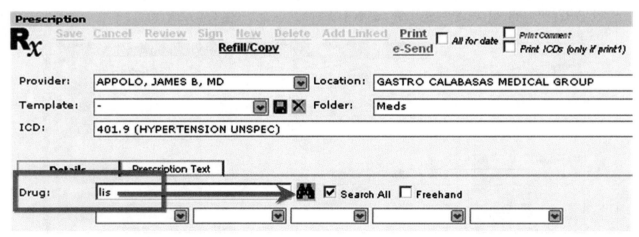

Reprinted with permission of TriMed Technologies, Corp.

10. Click on the radio button to the left of Search and then type hypertension in the description field and then press Enter on your keyboard.

Reprinted with permission of TriMed Technologies, Corp.

11. The ICD code, 401.9, is now populated in the field for ICD.

12. Beneath the Drug tab, in field next to Drug, enter "lis" (the first three letters of the drug to be prescribed) and then click on the binoculars to the right of the field (make sure that the box to the left of Search All has a checkmark in it).

Reprinted with permission of TriMed Technologies, Corp.

13. Scroll through the resulting list until you find Lisinopril 20 mg Tab. Click on it. The frequency, the form, and the route of administration will autopopulate based on your selection. The category of the drug will also autopopulate.

14. In the date field, type 10/07/2008.

15. In the field for Quantity, type 30. Note that when you do this, the field for Duration autopopulates.

16. In the Refills field, enter 6. This means that the patient can obtain six refills of this prescription before obtaining a new prescription.

17. Make sure the checkbox to the left of Current is selected. Check your work with the following screen shot.

Prescription

R x   Save   Cancel   Review   Sign   New   Delete   Add Linked   Print   ☐ All for date   ☐ Print Comment
               Refill/Copy   e-Send   ☐ Print ICDs (only if print1)

Provider: APPOLO, JAMES B, MD   ▼   Location: GASTRO CALABASAS MEDICAL GROUP

Template: -   ▼ ▣ ✗ Folder: Meds

ICD: 401.9 (HYPERTENSION UNSPEC)

| **Details** | Prescription Text |

Drug: Lisinopril   🔍 ☑ Search All ☐ Freehand

       20 mg ▼   QD ▼   Routine ▼   Tablet ▼   Oral ▼

       Interactions Leaflets Discontinued   *DrugID: 183474*   *DEAClass: 0*   *Drug Level: 0*

Date: 10/07/2008 ⊠   Category: ACE Inhibitors

Quantity: 30   Dur Days: 30   Refills: 6

Pharmacy
Instructions:
Packaging

Reprinted with permission of TriMed Technologies, Corp.

18. Click on Save. Note that the new prescription now appears in the Tree View, beneath today's appointment date. Proceed to Task 6-2.

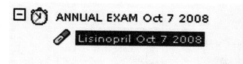

⊟ ⏱ ANNUAL EXAM Oct 7 2008
   🖉 Lisinopril Oct 7 2008

Reprinted with permission of TriMed Technologies, Corp.

TASK 6-2: SENDING A PRESCRIPTION FOR PROVIDER SIGN OFF

1. With the prescription saved, and the screen still open on it, click on the open envelope in the top right corner of the template. This action allows you to send a message to the provider, informing that the prescription is ready to be signed off.

Reprinted with permission of TriMed Technologies, Corp.

2. A new window will open. On the left side of the screen, beneath "select individual staff," highlight the admin entry that corresponds to your user login. For example, if your user login is "user15," the admin entry would be "admin15." (In a real medical office, you would select the patient's provider.)

3. With the Admin entry highlighted, click on the > button.

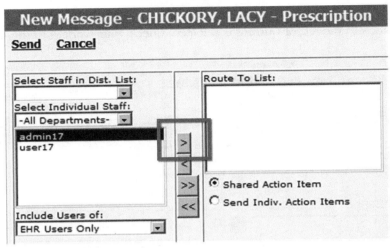

Reprinted with permission of TriMed Technologies, Corp.

4. This moves the Admin name into the Route To list. Click on this entry in the Route To list to select it.

5. Click on the radio button for Send Indiv. Action Items.

6. The Route Date and Time will autopopulate with the current date and time.

7. In the Action Type field, use the drop-down menu to select Sign Off.

8. Leave the Priority as Normal.

9. The Attachment/Routed Item is autopopulated with the prescription information. Check your work with the following screen shot.

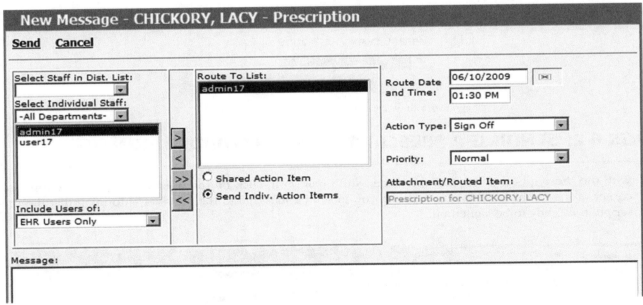

Reprinted with permission of TriMed Technologies, Corp.

10. Click Send. Now you are back on the prescription screen. Minimize the screen by clicking on that same button on the right side of the screen. Click on the X next to Lisinopril to close out of the screen.

11. Click the Home button to return to the EHR schedule.

⬤ PUTTING IT ALL TOGETHER

TASK 6-3: CREATING PRESCRIPTIONS AND ROUTING TO THE PROVIDER FOR SIGN OFF

This task requires you to create prescriptions and route them to the provider for authorization without using step-by-step instructions as given in the previous tasks.

Today is October 15, 2008. Harold Katt is a patient of Dr. Appolo.

1. Using the steps learned in Module 4, indicate on the appointment schedule that the patient has Arrived and Registered. (The patient has no registration updates.)

2. Then, open the EHR Home Page, and using the steps learned in Module 5, indicate on the EHR schedule that the patient has been Admitted.

3. Create a new Prescription for Mr. Katt using the information prescribed from Dr. Appolo (the following list), and route it for provider approval.

   • Diagnosis: Hyperlipidemia (272.4)
   • Medication: Lipitor
   • Dosage: 40 mg tablets
   • Frequency: Once per day
   • Quantity: 30
   • Refills: 11

Today is November 5, 2008. Candice Jones is a patient of Dr. Appolo, who has prescribed medication for her back pain related to an injury two weeks ago.

1. Using the steps learned in Module 4, indicate on the appointment schedule that the patient has Arrived and Registered. (The patient has no registration updates.)

2. Then, open the EHR Home Page, and using the steps learned in Module 5, indicate on the EHR schedule that the patient has been Admitted.

3. Create a new Prescription for Ms. Jones using the information prescribed from Dr. Appolo (the following list), and route it for provider approval.

   • Diagnosis: Backache (724.5)
   • Medication: Carisoprodol
   • Dosage: 250 mg tablets
   • Frequency: Once per day
   • Quantity: 14
   • Refills: 0

Recording Therapeutic Injections and Immunizations

OBJECTIVES

In this module, you will:

1. Document administration of therapeutic injections ordered by the provider and administered by the medical assistant.

2. Complete a superbill for the administration of therapeutic injections.

TASK 7-1: DOCUMENTING ADMINISTRATION OF A THERAPEUTIC INJECTION FOR JODIE MILLER

Today is October 28, 2008.

Jodie Miller is a patient of Dr. Zues and is coming in today at 10 a.m. for an injection for her rheumatoid arthritis (714.0). She is seeing only the MA today; there will be no physician visit. Dr. Zues has ordered 3 mg of Celestone to be administered to the patient.

1. Log in to e-Medsys®.

2. Using the steps learned in Module 4, indicate on the appointment schedule that the patient has Arrived and Registered. (The patient has no registration updates.)

3. Then, open the EHR Home Page, and using the steps learned in Module 5, indicate on the EHR schedule that the patient has been Admitted.

4. Double click on Jodie's appointment on the EHR schedule to bring up Jodie's chart.

5. In Jodie's chart, on the left side of the screen, right click on today's appointment.

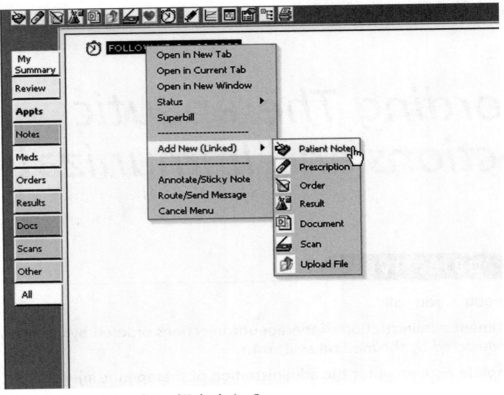

Reprinted with permission of TriMed Technologies, Corp.

6. Select Add New (Linked) ▶ and then Patient Note. The new Note appears on the right side of the screen. You may enlarge the note if you prefer.

7. The Provider, Department, Template Type, and Folder are autopopulated. Be sure that in the Template field None is selected.

8. In the ICD field, click on the binoculars to search for rheumatoid arthritis.

9. With the radio button next to Search selected, type rheu and press Enter on your keyboard. Now the ICD field is populated with the correct code, 714.0.

10. Enter the date of administration, 10/28/2008.

11. In the Comments section, type "3 mg of Celestone administered by *<insert your name and credentials>*, per Dr. Zues."

12. Check your work with the following screen shot and then click Save.

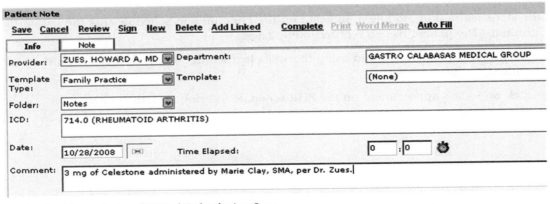

Reprinted with permission of TriMed Technologies, Corp.

13. When you are certain that the information documented is accurate, you will sign off on this note. Click Sign.

14. A new window opens. *Your sign off password is your user Login* (the one that you logged into e-Medsys® with; for example, "user15"). Enter your user Login and click Save.

Sign Off Patient Note

Save   Cancel

Enter Password: ●●●●●●

☐ Don't Prompt For Signoff Password (this session)

Reprinted with permission of TriMed Technologies, Corp.

15. Now the information that you entered appears grayed out on the screen. This information is part of the patient's permanent record and cannot be further modified.

Note: You must complete this Task and sign off on the note in order to continue to Task 7-2.

TASK 7-2: COMPLETING A SUPERBILL FOR JODIE MILLER

Complete a superbill indicating the diagnosis of rheumatoid arthritis (714.0), the administration of the drug (90782), and the supply of Celestone (J0702).

1. Still in Jodie Miller's chart, on the left side of the screen, left click on the 10/28/2008 FOLLOW UP appointment, highlighting it.

My Summary

Review

Appts

Notes

FOLLOW UP Oct 28 2008

Oct 28 2008

Reprinted with permission of TriMed Technologies, Corp.

2. When you do this, the right side of the screen brings up more information regarding the appointment. From the right-hand corner of this screen, select the Superbill tab.

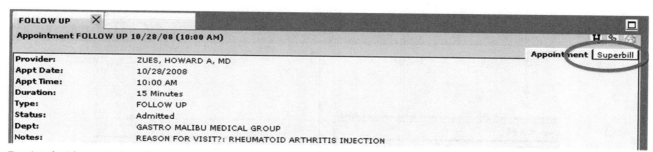

FOLLOW UP ☒	
Appointment FOLLOW UP 10/28/08 (10:00 AM)	
	Appointment | Superbill
Provider:	ZUES, HOWARD A, MD
Appt Date:	10/28/2008
Appt Time:	10:00 AM
Duration:	15 Minutes
Type:	FOLLOW UP
Status:	Admitted
Dept:	GASTRO MALIBU MEDICAL GROUP
Notes:	REASON FOR VISIT?: RHEUMATOID ARTHRITIS INJECTION

Reprinted with permission of TriMed Technologies, Corp.

3. The electronic superbill appears. Click on the corner box to enlarge while you are working within the superbill.

4. Make sure that Dr. Howard Zues's name appears in the Provider field. Leave the second provider field blank.

5. In the Date field, type 10/28/2008. The Insurance field is autopopulated based on the patient's insurance.

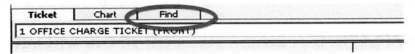

Reprinted with permission of TriMed Technologies, Corp.

6. Below the Comments section, there is a section with three tabs (Ticket, Chart, and Find). The Ticket tab is populated with some of the most common charges used in the medical office. If a charge does not appear on the Ticket tab, you can select the Find tab to look up a CPT code and add it to the superbill. Click on the Find tab.

Reprinted with permission of TriMed Technologies, Corp.

7. Type 90782 (the administration of the drug) and then press Enter on your keyboard.

8. Now the procedure code appears below the search field, with a box next to it. Click on the box to select it. When you do, a row at the bottom opens that indicates your selection.

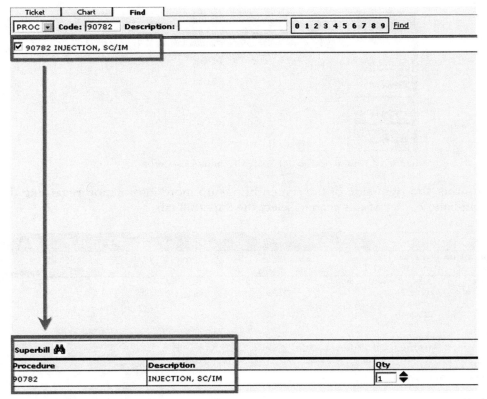

Reprinted with permission of TriMed Technologies, Corp.

9. Move your mouse into the Diag1 field. When you do, an icon of binoculars appears.

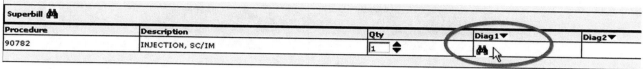

Reprinted with permission of TriMed Technologies, Corp.

10. Click on the binoculars. Now the cursor moves back up to the Code field. Type rheu in the Description field (to search for rheumatoid arthritis) and press Enter on your keyboard.

11. Now the diagnosis code appears below the search field, with a box next to it.

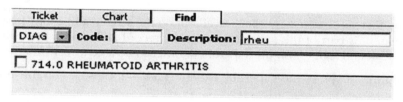

Reprinted with permission of TriMed Technologies, Corp.

12. Click on the box to select it. When you do, note that the diagnosis code now appears in the Diag1 box at the bottom.

13. Click Save. Now you are back on the Ticket tab.

14. The next CPT code is listed on the Ticket tab, so scroll down and select the box next to J0702 for the supply of Celestone. Note that when you select the box, a new row appears at the bottom.

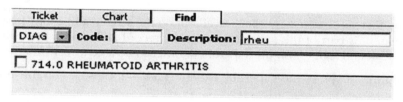

Reprinted with permission of TriMed Technologies, Corp.

15. Now, click on the triangle next to Diag1. This copies the diagnosis code that you had previously selected and enters it into the Celestone row.

Reprinted with permission of TriMed Technologies, Corp.

16. Click Save.

17. When you are certain that the information documented is accurate, you will sign off on these charges. Click Sign.

18. A new window opens. *Your sign off password is your user Login* (the one that you logged into e-Medsys®
    with; for example, "user15"). Enter your user Login and click Save.

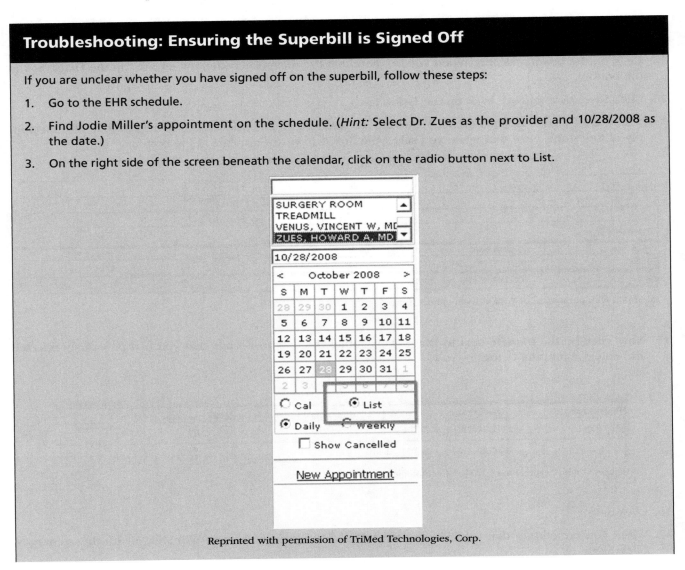

Reprinted with permission of TriMed Technologies, Corp.

19. Now the information that you entered appears grayed out on the screen, and a lock icon appears on the Super-
    bill tab. This information is part of the patient's permanent record and cannot be further modified. *Note:* You
    must complete this Task and sign off on the superbill in order to be able to perform the tasks in Module 9.

20. Now click Print to print a copy of the superbill. Label it Task 7-2. Close when finished.

Troubleshooting: Ensuring the Superbill is Signed Off

If you are unclear whether you have signed off on the superbill, follow these steps:

1. Go to the EHR schedule.

2. Find Jodie Miller's appointment on the schedule. (*Hint:* Select Dr. Zues as the provider and 10/28/2008 as
   the date.)

3. On the right side of the screen beneath the calendar, click on the radio button next to List.

Reprinted with permission of TriMed Technologies, Corp.

4. Now, the left side of the screen brings up the schedule in List view. In this view, there is a Superbill column. In this column, the status of the superbill is indicated:

   - *Signed* means the superbill has been signed off on.
   - *Saved* means the superbill has been created, but not signed off on.
   - If there is nothing in this column, the superbill has not been created.

5. If you have followed the steps in Task 7-2, the Superbill column for Jodie Miller should indicate *Signed*.

e-Medsys - EHR	Home	Chart	Web	Tools	Admin	Logout		User: user1

HOME PAGE

Schedule | Review | Messages | Sp

Schedule List - ZUES, HOWARD A, MD (1 appts)

Appt Start	Patient Name	Type	Status	Superbill	Department	Provider
7:30 AM		OUT	Open		GASTRO MALIBU MEDICAL GROUP	ZUES, HOWARD A, MD
7:45 AM		OUT	Open		GASTRO MALIBU MEDICAL GROUP	ZUES, HOWARD A, MD
8:00 AM		OUT	Open		GASTRO MALIBU MEDICAL GROUP	ZUES, HOWARD A, MD
8:15 AM		OUT	Open		GASTRO MALIBU MEDICAL GROUP	ZUES, HOWARD A, MD
8:30 AM		OUT	Open		GASTRO MALIBU MEDICAL GROUP	ZUES, HOWARD A, MD
8:45 AM		OUT	Open		GASTRO MALIBU MEDICAL GROUP	ZUES, HOWARD A, MD
9:00 AM		ANY	Open		GASTRO MALIBU MEDICAL GROUP	ZUES, HOWARD A, MD
9:15 AM		ANY	Open		GASTRO MALIBU MEDICAL GROUP	ZUES, HOWARD A, MD
9:30 AM		ANY	Open		GASTRO MALIBU MEDICAL GROUP	ZUES, HOWARD A, MD
9:45 AM		ANY	Open		GASTRO MALIBU MEDICAL GROUP	ZUES, HOWARD A, MD
10:00 AM	MILLER, JODIE S	F/U	Admitted	Signed	GASTRO MALIBU MEDICAL GROUP	ZUES, HOWARD A, MD
10:15 AM		ANY	Open		GASTRO MALIBU MEDICAL GROUP	ZUES, HOWARD A, MD
10:30 AM		ANY	Open		GASTRO MALIBU MEDICAL GROUP	ZUES, HOWARD A, MD
10:45 AM		ANY	Open		GASTRO MALIBU MEDICAL GROUP	ZUES, HOWARD A, MD
11:00 AM		ANY	Open		GASTRO MALIBU MEDICAL GROUP	ZUES, HOWARD A, MD
11:15 AM		ANY	Open		GASTRO MALIBU MEDICAL GROUP	ZUES, HOWARD A, MD
11:30 AM		ANY	Open		GASTRO MALIBU MEDICAL GROUP	ZUES, HOWARD A, MD
11:45 AM		ANY	Open		GASTRO MALIBU MEDICAL GROUP	ZUES, HOWARD A, MD

Reprinted with permission of TriMed Technologies, Corp.

6. If the column does not indicate *Signed*, go back into Jodie's chart. (*Hint:* Mouse over Chart on the top menu, and click on Jodie Miller from the drop-down list.) The superbill must be signed off on in order to complete Module 9.

PUTTING IT ALL TOGETHER

TASK 7-3: RECORDING ADMINISTRATION OF INJECTIONS AND CREATING SUPERBILLS

Without using step-by-step instructions as given in the previous tasks, this task requires you to (1) receive the patient (indicating Arrived and Registered on the schedule), (2) admit the patient using the EHR schedule, (3) create a new patient note to record the administration of injections, and (4) create and sign off on the superbill. *Note:* The superbill must be signed off on in order to complete Module 9.

1. On October 29, 2008, at 11:30 a.m., Crystal Nowell, a patient of Dr. Appolo, came in for her B-12 shot to be administered by the MA without a physician visit. Using the steps outlined in the earlier tasks and the information in the following list, document the administration of the injection and create a superbill for her. Print out the superbill and label it Task 7-3A.

   - Diagnosis: Vitamin B Deficiency
   - Diagnosis Code: 281.1
   - Administration Code: 90782
   - Substance Injected Code: J3420

2. Burt Ringer, a patient of Dr. Appolo, comes in the office for a tetanus shot on November 11, 2008, at 3 p.m. Using the steps outlined in the earlier tasks and the information in the following list, document the administration of the injection and create a superbill for him. Print out the superbill and label it Task 7-3B.

- Diagnosis: Need for tetanus vaccination
- Diagnosis Code: V03.7
- Administration Code: 90782
- Substance Administered Code: 90703

Ordering Laboratory Test and Entering Results

In this module, you will:

1. Record laboratory test orders in a patient record.

2. Send laboratory test orders to the provider for approval.

3. Upload the results of laboratory tests to a patient record.

TASK 8-1: RECORDING A LABORATORY TEST ORDER FOR DONALD BARR

Today is October 23, 2008.

Dr. Venus orders a lipid panel for Donald Barr to test for hyperlipidemia (272.4).

1. Log in to e-Medsys®.

2. Using the steps learned in Module 4, indicate on the appointment schedule that the patient has Arrived and Registered. (The patient has no registration updates.)

3. Then, open the EHR Home Page, and using the steps learned in Module 5, indicate on the EHR schedule that the patient has been Admitted.

4. Double click on Donald's appointment on the EHR schedule to bring up his chart.

5. In Donald's chart, on the lower left side of the screen, right click on today's appointment.

6. Select Add New (Linked) ► and then Order.

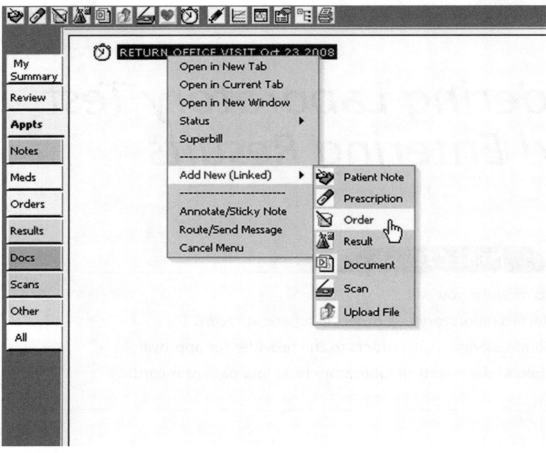

Reprinted with permission of TriMed Technologies, Corp.

7. The new Order appears on the lower right side of the screen. The Provider, Department, Folder, and Insurance fields are autopopulated.

8. In the date field, enter 10/23/2008.

9. The order will be billed to the patient's insurance company, so in the Bill To option, make sure the button to the left of Insurance is selected.

10. The Priority field has various drop-down options; select Routine. The remaining fields should be left blank. Check your screen with the following screen shot.

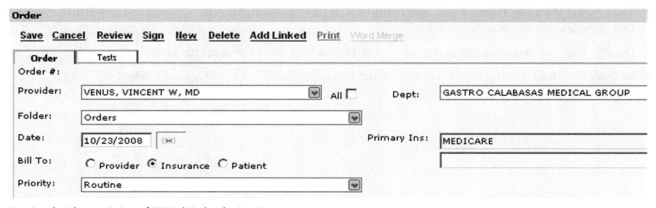

Reprinted with permission of TriMed Technologies, Corp.

11. Click Save.

12. Now, click on the Tests tab.

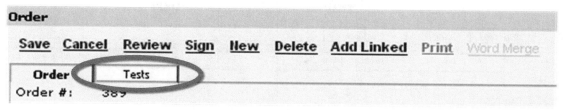

Reprinted with permission of TriMed Technologies, Corp.

13. In the Company field, select LabCorp from the drop-down menu. The Order Set field should be autopopulated with "LabCorp Test Set."

14. From the Set Tests tab, scroll down and click in the box to the left of LIPID (Lipid Panel w-Chol).

15. Note that when you select the Lipid panel, a row appears at the bottom of the screen, which indicates your selection.

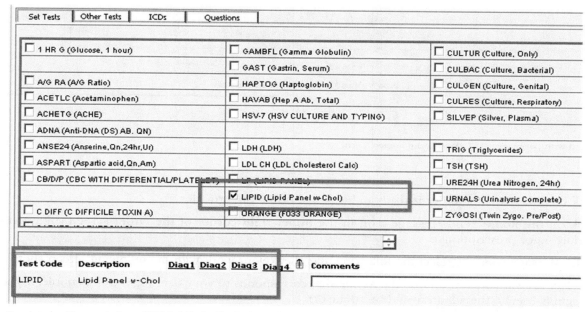

Reprinted with permission of TriMed Technologies, Corp.

16. Now click the ICD tab.

17. Type "hyp" in the Desc field, and press Enter on your keyboard. This searches for all diagnosis codes that start with these letters.

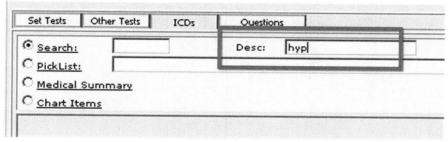

Reprinted with permission of TriMed Technologies, Corp.

18. Click in the box to the left of 272.4 HYPERLIPIDEMIA NEC/NOS. Note that when you select the box, the diagnosis code is filled in the row at the bottom in the Diag1 field.

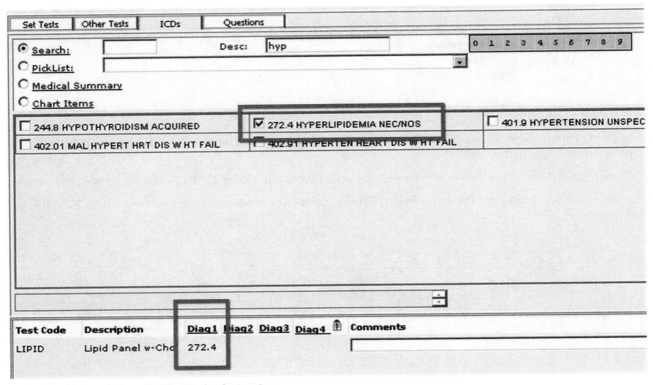

Reprinted with permission of TriMed Technologies, Corp.

19. Click on Save. Now the order is ready to be signed off by the provider.

20. Click on the Route/Send Message icon in the upper right corner of the Order screen (like you did in Module 6, for prescriptions).

21. In the Message window, select the following and check your work with the following screen shot:

- Select Individual Staff: Choose the Admin that corresponds to your User login (for example, if your user login is user17, the admin would be admin17).
- Route to: Choose the admin that corresponds to your user login.
- The Date and Time automatically populate; leave this as today's date.
- Action Type: Select "Sign Off" from the drop-down list.
- Priority: Select "Normal" from the drop-down list.

New Message - BARR, DONALD - Order

Send Cancel

Select Staff in Dist. List:

Select Individual Staff:
-All Departments-

admin17
user17

Include Users of:
EHR Users Only

Route To List:
admin17

>
<
>>
<<

○ Shared Action Item
◉ Send Indiv. Action Items

Route Date and Time: 06/10/2009   04:37 PM ✉

Action Type: Sign Off

Priority: Normal

Attachment/Routed Item:
Order for BARR, DONALD

Message:

Reprinted with permission of TriMed Technologies, Corp.

22. Click on Send. The order has now been sent to the provider for approval. Click on the Home link at the top of the screen to return to the EHR Schedule.

 # PUTTING IT ALL TOGETHER

TASK 8-2: RECORDING LABORATORY TEST ORDERS

This task requires you to record a laboratory test orders without using step-by-step instructions as given in the previous tasks.

Dr. Medusa orders a One-Hour Glucose Test for Ashley Mansfield on October 30, 2008. When you have entered the ordered test and saved it, send the order to be signed off on.

- Test Ordered: 1 HR G
- Diagnosis: Diabetes (250.00)

TASK 8-3: UPLOADING LABORATORY RESULTS INTO THE PATIENT CHART

Today is November 4, 2008.

Donald Barr's lipid panel results have come back from the laboratory. The results are scanned in and need to be uploaded to the patient's chart. (*Note:* in a medical office, results are often sent electronically and directly recorded to the patient's record.) Here we will simulate receiving laboratory results that were received by the office as a hard copy fax.

Special Note: Prior to Starting Task 8-3

In order to complete this activity, as well as Task 8-4, you will need to retrieve two documents from this workbook's Online Companion: "Task 8-3: Laboratory Results" and "Task 8-4: Laboratory Results." Please follow these steps:

1.   Go to this Web site: www.delmarlearning.com/companions.

2.   Click on Allied Health from the left navigation bar.

Reprinted with permission of TriMed Technologies, Corp.

3.   Scroll down and click on the title of this book, *The Total Practice Management Workbook: Using e-Medsys®* Educational Edition.

4.   Click on Student Resources on the left navigation bar.

5.   Click on the file, Task 8-3: Laboratory Results. Save the file to a place of your choice (such as a flash drive or the desktop), where you can easily retrieve it for this activity.

6.   Click on the file, Task 8-4: Laboratory Results. Save the file to a place of your choice (such as a flash drive or the desktop), where you can easily retrieve it for the next activity.

7.   You are ready to begin Task 8-3.

1. Log in to e-Medsys®.

2. Click on EHR Home Page from the drop-down box. This action opens the EHR home page in a new window. From the menu along the top of the page, click on Chart.

3. Search for Donald Barr (either by typing the patient's last name and clicking Enter, or by clicking the first letter of the patient's last name along the left side of the screen).

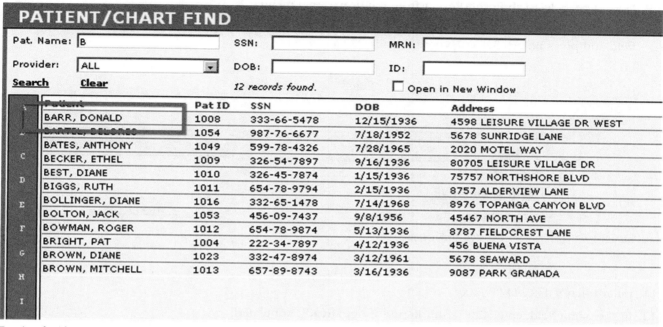

Reprinted with permission of TriMed Technologies, Corp.

4. Double click on the patient's name to open his chart.

5. From the left tab, click on Appts. You should see Donald's appointment on 10/23/2008, as well as the Order that is linked to that appointment.

6. Right click on the Order from 10/23/2008. Select Add New (Linked) ▶ and then Upload File.

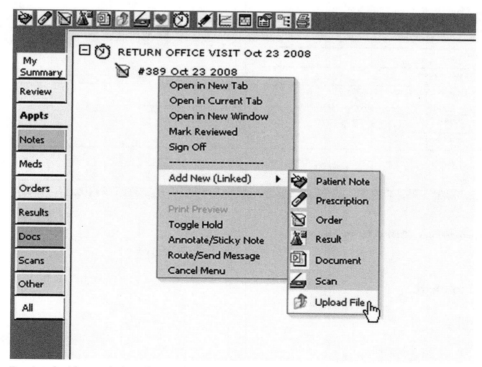

Reprinted with permission of TriMed Technologies, Corp.

7. The Document upload appears on the right side of the screen.

8. Folder: Select Results from the drop-down menu.

9. Doc. Type: Select Lab Result Report from the drop-down menu.

10. In the ICD field, click the binoculars and search for Hyperlipidemia (*hint:* type "hyp" in the description field and press Enter). Select Hyperlipidemia 272.4.

ICD:

○ Search: Desc: hyp   0 1 2 3 4 5 6 7 8 9

○ PickList:

○ Medical Summary

○ Chart Items   Cancel / Close

Reprinted with permission of TriMed Technologies, Corp.

11. Enter today's date, 11/04/2008.

12. In the name field, enter Lab Result Report if not already populated.

13. Leave the description field empty.

14. Next to the Document to Upload field, click Browse.

15. Locate and select the Task 8-3 Laboratory Results file that you downloaded from the Online Companion Web site. Check your work with the following screen shot.

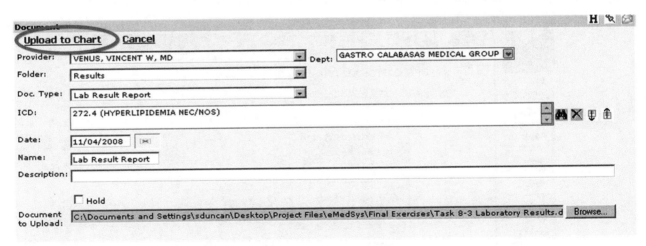

Reprinted with permission of TriMed Technologies, Corp.

16. Click Upload to Chart.

17. Now, on the left side of the screen, the Lab Result should appear in Tree View, as a submenu item beneath the 10/23/2008 Orders. Click on the Home link at the top of the screen to return to the EHR Schedule.

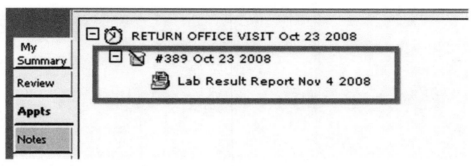

Reprinted with permission of TriMed Technologies, Corp.

PUTTING IT ALL TOGETHER

TASK 8-4: UPLOADING LABORATORY TEST RESULTS

This task requires you to record laboratory test results without using step-by-step instructions as given in the previous tasks.

Upload the laboratory results document (received today, November 12, 2008) for Ashley Mansfield's glucose test which was performed on October 30.

> To complete this activity, you will need to download the Task 8-4 Laboratory Results file from the Online Companion Web site, if you have not done so already. See the Special Note box in this Module for directions.

MODULE **9**

Posting Patient Charges, Recording Payments, and Scheduling Follow-up Appointments

OBJECTIVES

In this module, you will:

1. Post procedure charges to patient accounts from a charge ticket.
2. Post procedure charges to patient accounts using the electronic data interface (EDI) feature.
3. Post payments (credits) to patient accounts.
4. Create CMS-1500 forms to submit to insurance carriers.
5. Create patient receipts.
6. Schedule return appointments at the conclusion of the patient visit.

TASK 9-1: POSTING CHARGES FOR PERRY MARSHALL

Today is November 25, 2008.

Perry Marshall suffers from diverticulosis (562.10), and Dr. Venus performed a sigmoidoscopy (45330).

1. Log in to e-Medsys®.
2. At the top of the screen, click on Billing.

3. Click on Posting from the drop-down box and then Charge Posting from the side drop-down box. (*Note:* The keyboard shortcut for this is Ctrl + H.)

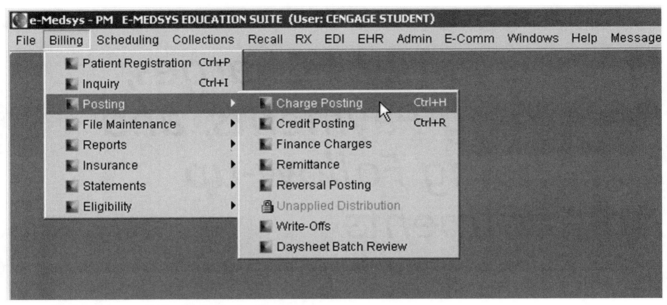

Reprinted with permission of TriMed Technologies, Corp.

4. A Batch Posting window will appear. Enter the New Batch Description: CHARGES FOR 11/25/2008. (*Note:* Each office will have a policy for posting charges. Always follow specific office policy. For the purposes of these exercises, we will be posting procedures organized by "day.")

5. Select GASTRO CALABASAS MEDICAL GROUP from the drop-down list. This selection indicates the location of the person entering the charges—not the location of where the patient was seen. The location of where each patient was seen is part of the individual charge postings. For the purposes of these exercises, you should select Gastro Calabasas Medical Group as your posting location.

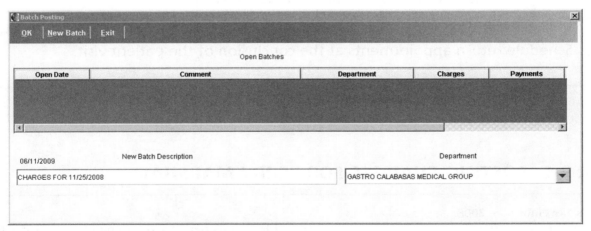

Reprinted with permission of TriMed Technologies, Corp.

6. Click OK. Now the Batch name appears at the top of the Charge Posting screen.

7. Type the patient's last name (MARSHALL) in the Name field, and then click Search.

Reprinted with permission of TriMed Technologies, Corp.

8. A charge ticket was not created for this patient, so click Cancel at the next prompt.

9. Now the cursor is at the bottom part of the window, in the Charge tab. Enter the following information:
   - Date: 11/25/2008
   - Department: Gastro Calabasas Medical Group
   - Provider: Dr. Venus
   - Primary Insurance Plan: Aetna (this is already populated from the selection in the patient registration screen)
   - Referring Provider: Leave blank

Charge	2nd Provider	DX +	POS	Auth	ECS Comment	Dates	UB	Prin. Proc.	Anesth	General Comment	Recall

Date	Department	Provider	Primary Ins Plan
11/25/2008	GASTRO CALABASAS MEDICAL GROUP ▼	VENUS, VINCENT W, MD ▼	AETNA

Reprinted with permission of TriMed Technologies, Corp.

10. In the Procedure field, type % and press Enter on your keyboard. This is a search function of the program and allows you to search for all Procedure codes that are in the system.

11. Select 45330 from the list and click OK.

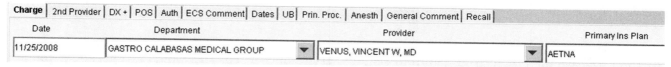

Number	CPT	Desc
85	85025	COMPLETE CBC
89	80053	COMPLETE METABOLIC PANEL
33	99386	COMPLETE PHYSICAL EXAM
63	9999	COMPLETE PHYSICAL PANEL
88	82550	CPK
11	45378	DIAGNOSTIC COLONOSCOPY
40	45330	DIAGNOSTIC SIGMOIDOSCOPY
45	20605	DRAIN/INJECT, JOINT/BURSA
43	10060	DRAINAGE OF SKIN ABSCESS
23	36415	DRAWING BLOOD
58	90701	DTP VACCINE, IM
39	93231	ECG MONITOR/RECORD, 24 HRS
38	93230	ECG MONITOR/REPORT, 24 HRS
79	76805	ECHO EXAM OF PREGNANT UTERUS
35	93000	EKG
116	97032	ELECTRICAL STIMULATION
102	82670	ESTRADIOL
111	44392SG	F/F COLONOSCOPY & POLYPECTOMY
112	45910SG	F/F DILATION OF RECTAL NARROWING
110	45333SG	F/F SIGMOIDOSCOPY & POLYPECTOMY
107	43247SG	F/F UPPER GI ENDOSCOPY
108	43239SG	F/F UPPER GI ENDOSCOPY, BIOPSY
109	43235SG	F/F UPPR GI ENDOSCOPY, DIAGNOSIS
75	FINANCE	FINANCE CHARGE
60	90659	FLU VACCINE, WHOLE, IM
93	84439	FREE TSH
103	83001	FSH

Reprinted with permission of TriMed Technologies, Corp.

12. In the DX-1 field (Diagnosis), type % and press Enter on your keyboard. Select the diagnosis 562.10 and click OK.

13. Now the program automatically opens another tab, where you can enter additional diagnosis codes (if the provider has specified these). Since there are no other diagnosis codes indicated by the provider, click the Return button.

14. You are back on the first tab, the Charge tab. Note that the POS, TOS, and Charge Amount have been filled in by the program, based on your code selections.

15. Keep the check boxes next to STMT (Statement), INS (Insurance), and AA (Accept Assignment) checked.

Reprinted with permission of TriMed Technologies, Corp.

16. You can leave the box next to Return to Date of Service unchecked. This would be checked if you are posting multiple services done on different dates, for example, hospital charges.

17. Click on the OK button. When you do, the information you just entered is now transferred below.

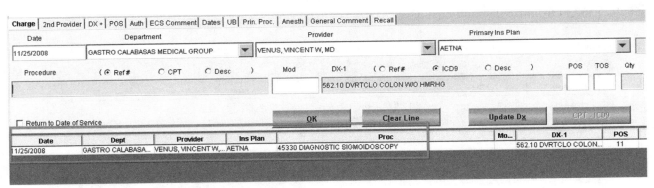

Reprinted with permission of TriMed Technologies, Corp.

You have been working in the Charge tab of this screen. You will note that there are several other tabs that are available on this screen. You have already seen the DX+ screen in the previous screen shot. We will discuss two additional screens. This is for your information only; you are not required to enter any data in these tabs for this exercise.

- **POS Tab:** This tab will pull forward for completion if POS is anything other than office (POS 11). This is a table look-up field.

- **Auth Tab:** If an authorization has been entered for this patient, for the posted procedure, this tab will display proposing the authorization number that was entered in the authorization screen. An authorization number can be entered for this specific transaction at Charge Posting. Also, the authorization button is accessible from the charge posting screen so all authorizations can be viewed.

18. Now that you have finished entering all the procedure charges for this patient, go to the bottom left corner of your screen. Check the boxes next to Credits, Prt Receipt, and Prt Claim.

- **Credits:** Checking this box informs the system that a payment will be posted right after charges have been posted. Once the charges have been accepted, the system will automatically open the credit posting screen for this posting batch. After the payment is entered and accepted, the system will take you back to the screen you are currently on, the charge posting screen.
- **Prt Stmt:** Checking this box informs the system that a statement should be produced for this patient after charges and payments have been posted. This box should be left unchecked.
- **Prt Receipt:** Checking this box informs the system that a receipt should be produced for this patient (for only those charges and payments posted today).
- **Prt Claim:** Checking this box informs the system that a claim form should be produced for this patient after charges and payments have been posted.

Reprinted with permission of TriMed Technologies, Corp.

Troubleshooting: Minimizing the Bottom Toolbar

If you are working on a PC with a Windows operating system and you do not see the Credits, Prt Receipt, Prt Stmt, and Prt Claim selections on the bottom left corner of the screen, it may be because they are "hidden" behind the bottom Start Menu toolbar (see the following screen shot).

Reprinted with permission of TriMed Technologies, Corp.

Minimize the bottom toolbar by:

1. Mouse over to the Start Menu toolbar.

2. Hover over the top part of the toolbar, and your cursor should change to an icon that looks like an up and down arrow.

3. Hold down the left click and drag the toolbar down, out of the screen. You should then see the bottom of the e-Medsys® screen with the Credits, Prt Receipt, Prt Stmt, and Prt Claim selections.

19. Now click the Accept button on the top Charge Posting menu. The charges will be accepted, and the program will automatically take you to the credit posting screen. Continue to Task 9-2 immediately.

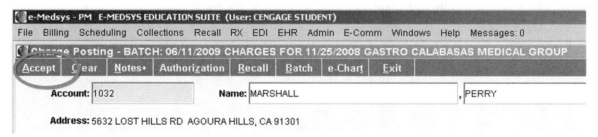

Reprinted with permission of TriMed Technologies, Corp.

TASK 9-2: POSTING A CO-PAYMENT FOR PERRY MARSHALL

Perry Marshall's co-payment is $45, and he also has an outstanding balance of $25 in the system. He writes a check (#1257) for $70, to be applied to today's co-payment and the outstanding balance.

1. You are now working in the Credit Posting screen. Your cursor should be in the Credit Info tab (which is the main screen on this page), in the date field. The date is already populated for you.

2. Under Credit Type, use the drop-down to select Check.

3. In the Check No field, type: 1257.

4. In the amount field, type: 70.00.

5. Now click the radio button next to All. When you do, two service dates appear below.

Date	Dept Prov	Proc DX	Qty	Chg Amt
03/01/2002	GASTCA VENU	99204 OFFICE/...	1	175.00
11/25/2008	GASTCA VENU	45330 DIAGNO...	1	225.00

Reprinted with permission of TriMed Technologies, Corp.

6. In the Applied column, enter $25.00 in the first row, for the 3/1/2002 charge. Enter $45.00 in the second row, for today's charges.

Date	Dept Prov	Proc DX	Qty	Chg Amt	Allowed	Approved	Paid%	Applied
03/01/2002	GASTCA VENU	99204 OFFICE/...1		175.00	0.00	0.00	0.00	25.00
11/25/2008	GASTCA VENU	45330 DIAGNO...1		225.00	0.00	0.00	0.00	45.00

Reprinted with permission of TriMed Technologies, Corp.

7. Click the Accept button in the upper left corner to apply the payments to Perry's account. Recall that you had chosen to create a CMS-1500 and patient receipt in Task 9-1, so immediately these files will print to your local printer:

   • Label the first file (the CMS-1500 form) as Task 9-2A.
   • Label the second file (the patient receipt) as Task 9-2B.

8. When you have finished, you are back on the charge posting screen. If you had additional charges to post that day, you would continue posting. Click Exit to return to the main menu.

TASK 9-3: POSTING CHARGES, APPLYING A CO-PAYMENT, AND SCHEDULING A FOLLOW-UP APPOINTMENT FOR ELIZABETH GREENLEY

Today is October 16, 2008.

During Elizabeth Greenley's initial office visit, Dr. Medusa performed a comprehensive preventive medicine evaluation (CPT 99386 and ICD-9 V70.0). Elizabeth told Dr. Medusa that for the most part, she felt healthy but does occasionally feel fatigued (780.79). As a routine measure, Dr. Medusa ordered a CBC (85025), drawing blood (36415).

Elizabeth pays her $10 co-payment with cash. Dr. Medusa would like her to schedule a follow-up appointment in about a month.

1. Log in to e-Medsys®.

2. At the top of the screen, click on Billing.

3. Click on Posting from the drop-down box and then Charge Posting from the side drop-down box. (*Note:* The keyboard shortcut for this is Ctrl + H.) A Batch Posting window will appear.

4. Click on the New Batch button.

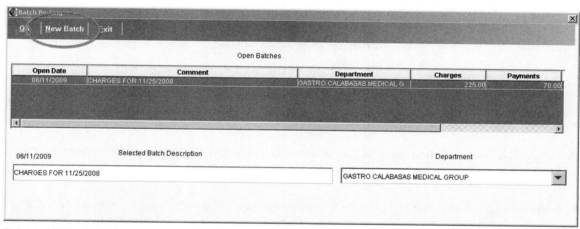

Reprinted with permission of TriMed Technologies, Corp.

5. Enter the New Batch Description: CHARGES FOR 10/16/2008. (*Note:* Each office will have a policy for posting charges. Always follow specific office policy. For the purposes of these exercises, we will be posting procedures organized by "day.")

6. Select GASTRO CALABASAS MEDICAL GROUP from the drop-down list. Remember that this selection indicates the location of the person entering the charges—not the location of where the patient was seen. The location of where each patient was seen is part of the individual charge postings. For the purposes of these exercises, you should select Gastro Calabasas Medical Group as your posting location. Click OK.

7. Type the patient's last name (Greenley) in the Name field, and then click Search.

8. Recall that a Charge Ticket was created for Elizabeth in Module 4, and the number on the upper left corner of the ticket is 1000138. Click OK. (*Note:* If the number on your charge ticket is different than the number listed here, that is OK, You should enter the number that appears on the upper left corner of the ticket that you printed.)

9. Note that when you do this, some information automatically populates on the charge posting screen—the date, the department, and the provider. You can proceed directly to entering the patient's procedures.

10. Above the Procedure field, select the button next to CPT. Type the CPT code in the field, 99386, and press Enter on your keyboard. (This is an alternative way to enter codes in these fields.)

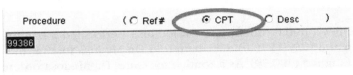

Reprinted with permission of TriMed Technologies, Corp.

11. Above the DX-1 field (Diagnosis), select the button next to ICD9. Type V70.0 and press Enter on your keyboard.

12. Now the program automatically opens another tab, where you can enter additional diagnosis codes (if the provider has specified these). Enter 780.79 in the DX-2 field for the diagnosis of fatigue.

13. Click the Return button to return to the Charge tab. Check your work with the following screen shot.

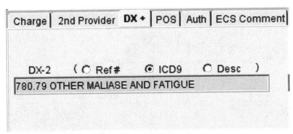

Reprinted with permission of TriMed Technologies, Corp.

14. Click on the OK button. When you do, the information you just entered is now transferred to the lower part of the screen.

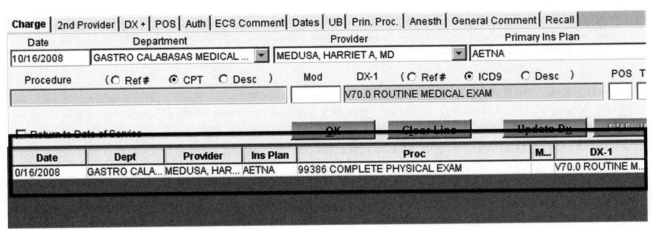

Reprinted with permission of TriMed Technologies, Corp.

15. Now, we will enter the next charge for the CBC. Type 85025 in the Procedure field and press Enter on your keyboard.

16. Note that the program has retained the first diagnosis code entered in the DX-1 field. However, we must change this to the fatigue diagnosis the provider has indicated. Move the mouse into the DX-1 field and delete the V70.0 diagnosis. Now type 780.79 and press Enter on your keyboard. Click OK to transfer the charge to the lower part of the screen.

17. Now enter the venipuncture charge (drawing blood, 36415). The diagnosis code is the same as the CBC entry and is automatically filled in for you. When you are finished, you should have three entries in the lower part of the screen, as shown in the following screen shot.

Date	Dept	Provider	Ins Plan	Proc
10/16/2008	GASTRO CALABASA...	MEDUSA, HARRIET A...AETNA		99386 COMPLETE PHYSICAL EXAM
10/16/2008	GASTRO CALABASA...	MEDUSA, HARRIET A...AETNA		85025 COMPLETE CBC
10/16/2008	GASTRO CALABASA...	MEDUSA, HARRIET A...AETNA		36415 DRAWING BLOOD

Reprinted with permission of TriMed Technologies, Corp.

18. Now that you have finished entering all the procedure charges for this patient, go to the bottom left corner of your screen. Check the boxes next to Credits, Prt Receipt, and Prt Claim. (*Hint:* If you do not see the Credits, Prt Receipt, and Prt Claim selections, refer back to the Troubleshooting box earlier in this Module.)

Reprinted with permission of TriMed Technologies, Corp.

19. Click the Accept button on the top Charge Posting menu. The charges will be posted, and the program will automatically take you to the credit posting screen (since you checked the box next to Credits).

20. In the Credit Info tab (which is the main screen on this page), note that the date is already populated for you. Under Credit Type, Cash is already populated for you. In the amount field, type 10.00.

21. Now click the radio button next to Today's, since you are posting the co-payment for today's charges. When you do, the charges you just posted appear on the screen. Enter $10.00 in the first row, applying the $10 payment to the preventative exam charge.

Date	Dept Prov	Proc DX	Qty	Chg Amt	Allowed	Approved	Paid%	Applied
10/16/2008	GASTCA MEDU	99386 COMPL...	1	175.00	0.00	0.00	0.00	10.00
10/16/2008	GASTCA MEDU	85025 COMPL...	1	20.00	0.00	0.00	0.00	0.00
10/16/2008	GASTCA MEDU	36415 DRAWI...	1	15.00	0.00	0.00	0.00	0.00

Reprinted with permission of TriMed Technologies, Corp.

22. Click the Accept button in the upper left corner to post the payments to Elizabeth's account. Recall that you had chosen to create a CMS-1500 form and patient receipt, so immediately these files will print to your local printer:

- Label the first file (the CMS-1500 form) as Task 9-3A.
- Label the second file (the patient receipt) as Task 9-3B.

23. When you have finished, you are back on the charge posting screen. Click Exit.

24. Now, recall that the provider would like to see Elizabeth in about a month for a follow-up visit. Schedule a follow-up appointment for Elizabeth for November 20, 2008, at 10 a.m., using the steps you learned in Module 2. When the appointment is booked, the patient visit is complete.

	Thu (11/20/08) (1 Appts)		Fri (11/21/08) (0 Appts)	
	GASTCA OUT		IMMA OUT	
	GASTCA OUT		IMMA OUT	
	GASTCA OUT		IMMA OUT	
	GASTCA OUT		IMMA OUT	
	GASTCA OUT		IMMA OUT	
	GASTCA OUT		IMMA OUT	
	GASTCA ANY		IMMA ANY	
	GASTCA ANY		IMMA ANY	
	GASTCA ANY		IMMA ANY	
	GASTCA ANY		IMMA ANY	
	GREENLEY, ELIZAB:F/U		IMMA ANY	
	GASTCA ANY		IMMA ANY	

Number	Name	Visit Type	Time	Len	Home	Work	Cell
1060	GREENLEY, ELIZABETH	F/U	10:00 AM	15	(818)338-5436	(818)737-3200 x25	(818)537-2077

FOLLOW-UP AFTER ANNUAL EXAM

	GASTCA OUT		IMMA ANY	
	GASTCA OUT			
	GASTCA OUT			
	GASTCA OUT			
	GASTCA OUT			
	GASTCA OUT			
	GASTCA ANY			
	GASTCA ANY			

Reprinted with permission of TriMed Technologies, Corp.

⊚ PUTTING IT ALL TOGETHER

TASK 9-4: POSTING CHARGES, APPLYING CO-PAYMENTS, AND SCHEDULING FOLLOW-UP APPOINTMENTS

This task requires you to post charges, apply co-payments, and schedule follow-up appointments for the following patients without using step-by-step instructions as given in the previous tasks. You will print out CMS-1500 forms and patient receipts and label them as indicated below.

1. Wilma Flint had an appointment with Dr. Appolo on October 27, 2008, to discuss her menopausal symptoms (627.9). He performed a problem-focused exam, and his medical decision making was straight forward (99212). Her insurance does not require a co-payment at the time of service, but she would like to pay $25 for an outstanding charge on 3/1/02. She writes check #3665 for $25.00. Schedule a follow-up appointment for December 17, 2008, at 11:30 a.m.

   • Label the first file (the CMS-1500 form) as Task 9-4-1A.
   • Label the second file (the patient receipt) as Task 9-4-1B.

2. Ashley Mansfield is a diabetic (250.00) and sees Dr. Medusa on October 30, 2008, for a blood glucose test (82948), drawing blood (36415). She does not pay a co-payment for this visit, so it is unnecessary to print a receipt for the patient (*Hint:* only the box next to Prt Claim will be checked). While she is at the office, she schedules a return office visit appointment (*Hint:* RET OV) for January 13, 2009, at 9:00 a.m.

   • Label the CMS-1500 form as Task 9-4-2.

TASK 9-5: POSTING CHARGES FOR JODIE MILLER USING THE ELECTRONIC DATA INTERFACE (EDI)

Today is October 28, 2008.

Jodie Miller, a patient of Dr. Zues, received an injection for her rheumatoid arthritis today. All charges will be billed to the patient's insurance; the patient will not be making a payment today.

1. Log in to e-Medsys®.

2. At the top of the screen, click on EDI.

3. Click on Charge Posting Interface from the drop-down box.

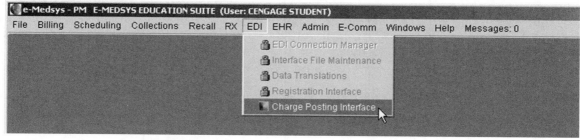

Reprinted with permission of TriMed Technologies, Corp.

4. A new window, Interface Charges, appears. On the bottom of the screen, select Dr. Zues as the physician from the drop-down. Leave the other drop-down fields as ALL.

5. Enter 10/28/2008 in the From and To fields and select the radio button next to Service Date. Check your work with the following screen shot.

Reprinted with permission of TriMed Technologies, Corp.

6. Click Search. The program should find Jodie Miller and display her information as a row on the top of the screen. If Jodie Miller does not appear, go back to Module 7 and ensure that you have signed off on her superbill. If the superbill is not signed off on, the charges will not appear.

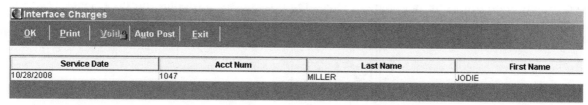

Reprinted with permission of TriMed Technologies, Corp.

7. Click on the row with Jodie's name to highlight it, and then click OK.

8. The program will bring you immediately to the charge posting screen. Click New Batch, and enter CHARGES FOR 10/28/2008 as the Batch name. Click OK.

9. Now, note that the program has already recorded the two charges (recall that you entered these charges on the Superbill while working in the patient's chart in Module 7).

Date	Dept	Provider	Ins Plan	Proc
10/28/2008	GASTRO MALIBU ME...	ZUES, HOWARD A, MD	CIGNA PPO	90782 INJECTION, SC/IM
10/28/2008	GASTRO MALIBU ME...	ZUES, HOWARD A, MD	CIGNA PPO	J0702 CELESTONE INJ PER 3 MG

Reprinted with permission of TriMed Technologies, Corp.

10. All the procedure charges have been posted for this patient automatically, so go to the bottom left corner of your screen. Check the box next to Prt Claim only, since the patient will not be making a payment today and does not need a receipt. (*Hint:* If you do not see the Prt Claim selection, refer back to the Troubleshooting box earlier in this Module.)

☐ Credits ☐ Prt Stmt ☐ Prt Receipt ☑ Prt Claim

Reprinted with permission of TriMed Technologies, Corp.

12. Click Accept to post the charges to the patient's account. The CMS-1500 form will print to your local printer. Label it Task 9-5.

13. Click Exit on the Interface Charges screen to return to the main menu.

TASK 9-6: POSTING CHARGES USING THE EDI AND APPLYING PAYMENTS

Today is October 29, 2008.

Crystal Nowell, a patient of Dr. Appolo, came in for a B-12 shot today. She does not have insurance and writes a check (#2232) for $45.00, the total amount of the visit.

1. Log in to e-Medsys®.

2. At the top of the screen, click on EDI. Click on Charge Posting Interface from the drop-down box.

3. In the Interface Charges window, select Dr. Appolo as the physician and 10/29/2008 as the Service Dates (*Hint:* both From and To), and click Search.

4. Select Crystal and click OK to bring the charges into the charge posting screen. Create a new batch, CHARGES FOR 10/29/2008.

5. When the program brings up her charges, check the boxes next to Credits and Prt Receipt. (*Hint:* If you do not see the Credits and Prt Receipt selections, refer back to the Troubleshooting box earlier in this Module.)

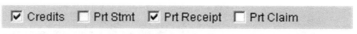

☑ Credits ☐ Prt Stmt ☑ Prt Receipt ☐ Prt Claim

Reprinted with permission of TriMed Technologies, Corp.

6. Click Accept. The program brings you directly to the Credit Posting screen (as you had selected on the previous screen).

7. Complete the following fields on this screen:

   - Be sure CHECK is selected as payment type.
   - Enter the Check Number, 2232.
   - Enter the Check amount, $45.00.

8. Click on the radio button next to Today's to bring up the charges posted on this date.

9. Now, apply the $45.00 to the two charges listed on the screen. Apply $20.00 to the first row, and $25.00 to the second row.

Date	Dept Prov	Proc DX	Qty	Chg Amt	Allowed	Approved	Paid%	Applied
10/29/2008	GASTCA APPO	90782 INJECTI...	1	20.00	0.00	0.00	0.00	20.00
10/29/2008	GASTCA APPO	J3420 VITAMIN...	1	25.00	0.00	0.00	0.00	25.00

Reprinted with permission of TriMed Technologies, Corp.

10. Click Accept. The receipt will print to your local printer. Label it Task 9-6.

11. Click Exit on the Interface Charges screen to return to the main menu.

⊙ PUTTING IT ALL TOGETHER
TASK 9-7: POSTING CHARGES USING THE EDI

This task requires you to post charges for the following patient without using step-by-step instructions as given in the previous task. The charges will be billed to the patient's insurance; the patient will not make a payment today.

1. Burt Ringer, a patient of Dr. Appolo, had a tetanus shot on November 11, 2008. Use the EDI charge posting interface to post the charges. Print the CMS-1500 form and label it Task 9-7.

Putting It All Together

OBJECTIVE

This module is designed to apply the skills you have learned to several patient case studies, without the step-by-step instruction given in the previous modules.

CASE STUDY 10-1

Jeffery Collingsworth

Today is October 1, 2008.

Jeffery Collingsworth calls today to schedule an appointment for an annual exam. He is new to the practice and would like to select Dr. Vincent Venus as his primary care provider.

Task 1: Adding a New Patient and Appointment Scheduling

Schedule an appointment for a new patient, Jeffery Collingsworth, on October 14, 2008, at 9:30 a.m. with Dr. Venus. You will need to add some registration information to add the patient into the database prior to scheduling the appointment for him.

1. Open the Patient Registration screen where you can record information from the patient. At this time, you need to record only the fields on the Patient Registration screen labeled in red. The remainder of the information will be recorded when Jeffery comes into the office and completes the registration paperwork. (*Hint:* Click OK through the prompts indicating that Work and Emergency phone numbers are recommended; these fields will be completed when the patient comes into the office.)

- Name: COLLINGSWORTH, JEFFERY
- Address: 87436 West Columbia Parkway, Pasadena, CA 90039
- Home Phone: (818) 555-1615
- Social Security Number: 222-45-9073

117

- Date of Birth: 08/16/1974
- Gender: Male

2. Click on Accept. You will complete the information when the patient comes in for his appointment.

3. Jeffery indicates that October 14, 2008, at 9:30 a.m. would be perfect for his annual exam. (*Hint:* Because he is a new patient, in the Visit Type field, click on the drop-down arrow and select NP. In the Reason for Visit field on the Supplemental Information screen, type Annual Exam.) Complete booking his appointment as you have done in previous Modules.

Task 2: Receiving the Patient and Completing Registration Information

Today is October 14, 2008.

Jeffery Collingsworth arrives 15 minutes early for his appointment. Indicate on the appointment schedule that Jeffery has arrived to the practice. Upon his arrival, Jeffery presents the registration forms he was sent in the mail. While Jeffery is waiting to see Dr. Venus, you record the information, completing his registration.

1. Find Jeffery's appointment on the schedule.

2. Right click on his appointment time and indicate that he has arrived. The color highlighting the time slot with his name will change to show that he has arrived.

3. Find Jeffery's account in Patient Registration. Using the following information, complete the patient's registration.

Employer	JCS Architects & Design
Work Phone	818-758-4412 x389
Cell Phone	998-443-8923
Emergency Contact	Joshua Colllingsworth, 818-768-3578
Marital Status	Single
Relationship to Guarantor	Self

4. Click on Accept + Ins.

5. You are now on the Insurance tab for Patient Registration. Select Add Ins from the list on the right of the screen. Enter the following information:

Insurance Plan	Blue Shield of CA (use the Red Bluff address)
Relationship to Policyholder	Self
Effective Date	01/01/2006
Group Number	AD9043
Policy Number	092836582

6. Leave the remaining fields as they are and click on Accept.

7. A Yes or No window will appear asking if you want to update the patient's charges with the new insurance information you have entered. Click on Yes.

8. Click on the tab for Guarantor and verify that the information entered on previous screens has transferred correctly and click on Accept.

9. Return to the appointment scheduling screen and indicate on the schedule that the patient is now Registered.

Task 3: Linking a New Note to an Appointment and Entering Chart Information

Jeffery is now taken back to an exam room.

1. Find Jeffery's appointment on the EHR schedule and indicate that he is now Admitted.

2. Right click on Jeffery's appointment on the EHR schedule, and use the menu to link a New Note to his chart for today's visit (October 14, 2008).

3. On the Information tab in the Notes, use the drop-down menu to select the Routine Exam Male template. Change the date to 10/14/2008.

4. Enter the following information on the Pt Info screen and click Save.

Chief Complaint	Annual Physical Exam
Problem List	Asthma
Surgical History	Tonsillectomy & Adenoidectomy @ 6 years old
Family History	Mom alive—56 years old, no chronic illnesses; Father alive and well at 58 years of age; two brothers and three sisters
Social History	Nonsmoker, social drinker, in long-term relationship for past 3 years, runs 15 miles per week on average and goes to gym four times per week

Task 4: Entering Information from Patient Questionnaire

Enter the information from the patient questionnaire form which Jeffery completed while he was in the waiting room.

1. Still in Jeffery Collingsworth's chart, select the ROS tab.

2. Enter information for Constitutional, Musculoskeletal, and Respiratory systems. All of this information will be reviewed with the patient and signed by Dr. Venus. Click on Save.

Constitutional	Normal
Musculoskeletal	Elbow stiffness
Respiratory	Asthma exacerbated by cold air and exposure to pet dander

Task 5: Entering Patient Vital Signs

Enter the vital signs that were taken upon bringing the patient into the exam room.

1. Still in Jeffery Collingsworth's chart, select the Exam tab.

2. Enter the vital signs in the appropriate fields and click Save. Now click the Print button. Label this printout as Case Study 10-1A.

Height	75 inches
Weight	205 pounds
Blood Pressure	118/68 (sitting)
Pulse	65
Respiration	18
Temperature	98.6

Provider Assessment for Jeffery Collingsworth

Dr. Venus has completed his examination of Jeffery. His assessment is as follows:

Normal, healthy 34-year-old male with no active concerns. Recommended ice on elbow and ibuprofen prophylactically for 2 weeks. Patient will schedule follow-up appointment in one month. Discussed proactive treatment of asthma symptoms; patient very educated on condition and treatment. Told patient to contact office when he needs a refill on his inhaler.

Task 6: Posting Charges

You will now enter the charges for Jeffery's visit.

Task 6 Note: Manual or Electronic (EDI) Charge Posting

This task may be performed using manual charge posting (instructions given in Module 9, Task 9-1) or using the EDI (instructions given in Module 9, Task 9-5).

In order to use the EDI, your instructor must complete a superbill on the EHR side of the program. This simulates the documentation that a provider would complete. Step-by-step instructions are given in the instructor material on the Online Companion.

Otherwise, manual posting should be used to complete this exercise.

1. Create a New Batch: CHARGES FOR 10/14/2008. (As with other exercises, the department is listed as Gastro Calabasas Medical Group.)

2. Post charges for Jeffery Collingsworth:

   - Department: Gastro Calabasas Medical Group
   - Procedure code: 99385
   - Diagnosis code: V70.0

3. Check the box next to CMS-1500 at the bottom of the screen to generate a claim form for Jeffery's visit. (*Hint:* If you do not see the Prt Claim selection, refer back to the Troubleshooting box in Module 9.)

4. Print the CMS-1500 form and label it Case Study 10-1B.

Task 7: Scheduling a Follow-Up Appointment

Dr. Venus has indicated that he wants to see Jeffery in one month to check his elbow. Schedule a follow-up appointment (for elbow stiffness) on November 18, 2008 at 9:30 a.m.

CASE STUDY 10-2

Susie Daly

Susie Daly is a patient of Dr. James Appolo. She has been experiencing abdominal pain accompanied with nausea for the past several days. Her mother has called late on Tuesday, November 18, 2008, seeking an appointment with Dr. Appolo for the next day.

Task 1: Appointment Scheduling

Schedule an appointment (*Hint:* return office visit) for the patient at 9:30 a.m. on Wednesday, November 19, 2008.

Task 2: Receiving the Patient

Today is November 19, 2008. Indicate on the appointment schedule that the patient has arrived to the practice. Susie's mother indicates that there are no registration updates for the patient, and then indicate that the patient is registered on the appointment schedule.

Task 3: Linking a New Note to an Appointment

Indicate that the patient has been Admitted on the EHR schedule. Link a new Patient Note to the Appointment. Select Multisystem E&M as the Template type. (Remember to change the date on the Patient Note to 11/19/2008.)

Task 4: Entering Patient Vital Signs and Chief Complaint

On the General tab, enter the following vital signs information and chief complaint:

Height	54 inches
Weight	85 pounds
Blood Pressure	110/60 (sitting)
Pulse	75
Respiration	25
Temperature	101.6
Chief Complaint	Abdominal pain and nausea for past three days, increased pain upon eating any solid food, on scale of 1–10, pain is an 8.

Task 5: Entering Chart Information

On the PFSH/HPI tab, enter the following information. The provider will review this with the patient and develop the HPI.

Print the Patient Note and label it Case Study 10-2A.

Social History	Lives with both parents and two siblings; fifth-grade honor student at Jensen Middle School
Previous Medical History	Umbilical Hernia; Fx Left Wrist
Family History	Non-contributory

Provider Assessment for Susie Daly

Susie is suffering from gastroenteritis; advised her mother that Susie should follow clear liquid diet for next 2–3 days and gradually introduce more solid foods as tolerated. Mother was also instructed to call office if symptoms worsen.

Task 6: Posting Charges

Enter the charges for the patient's visit on November 19, 2008:

- Department: Gastro Calabasas Medical Group

- Procedure code: 99214 Established Patient

- Diagnosis code: 558.9 Gastroenteritis NOS

Check the box next to CMS-1500 at the bottom of the screen to generate a claim form for the patient's visit. Print the CMS-1500 form and label it Case Study 10-2B. (*Hint:* If you do not see the Prt Claim selection, refer back to the Troubleshooting box in Module 9.)

Task 6 Note: Manual or Electronic (EDI) Charge Posting

This task may be performed using manual charge posting (instructions given in Module 9, Task 9-1) or using the EDI Interface (instructions given in Module 9, Task 9-5).

In order to use the EDI Interface, your instructor must complete a superbill on the EHR side of the program. This simulates the documentation that a provider would complete. Step-by-step instructions are given in the instructor material on the Online Companion.

Otherwise, manual posting should be used to complete this exercise.

CASE STUDY 10-3

Steve Macguire

Steve has called because he has been experiencing pain in his right ankle for the past week after he fell off a ladder at home and landed on his side. He would like to schedule an appointment with Dr. Harriet Medusa, his PCP. Dr. Medusa has an opening at 9:00 a.m. on Tuesday, October 14, 2008. This visit will be considered a return office visit because Steve is an established patient of Dr. Medusa's.

Task 1: Appointment Scheduling

Schedule an appointment for the patient at 9:00 a.m. on Tuesday, October 14, 2008.

Task 2: Receiving the Patient

Today is October 14, 2008. Indicate on the appointment schedule that the patient has arrived to the practice. The patient has no registration updates.

Task 3: Linking a New Note to an Appointment and Entering Chart Information

Indicate that the patient has been Admitted on the EHR schedule. Link a new Patient Note to the Appointment. Select Multisystem E&M as the template type, and change the date to 10/14/2008.

Task 4: Entering Patient Vital Signs and Chief Complaint

On the General tab, enter the following vital signs information and chief complaint:

Height	69 inches
Weight	190 pounds
Blood Pressure	180/95 (sitting)
Pulse	75
Respiration	18
Temperature	98.6
Chief Complaint	Right ankle pain after fall from ladder one week ago. X-rays taken at ER on the day of fall indicated no fractures. Ankle pain is constant and is described as throbbing. Patient has tried using ibuprofen and receives some relief but is taking 400 mg every 4 hours and is beginning to experience nausea as a result.

Task 5: Entering Chart Information

On the PFSH/HPI tab, enter the following information. The provider will review this with the patient and develop the HPI.

 Print the Patient Note and label it Case Study 10-3A.

Social History	Married with two children both at home, nonsmoker, social drinker, no illicit drug use
Previous Medical History	Appendectomy, hypercholesterolemia, hypertension
Family History	Non-contributory

Provider Assessment for Steve Macguire

Steve is suffering from a sprained right ankle. Ankle was wrapped for support and patient was advised to limit use. Patient was advised to take 600 mg of ibuprofen every 6 hours with food and apply ice to his knee. Schedule follow-up appointment for 2 weeks, and if pain increases, patient should contact office for appointment to be seen sooner.

Task 6: Posting Charges

Recall that you created a batch for today's date. Add these charges to that batch—CHARGES FOR 10/14/2008. Enter the charges for the patient's visit on October 14, 2008:

- Department: Gastro Calabasas Medical Group
- Procedure code: 99214 Established Patient
- Diagnosis code: 845.09 Ankle Sprain

Check the box next to CMS-1500 at the bottom of the screen to generate a claim form for the patient's visit. Print the CMS-1500 form and label it Case Study 10-3B. (*Hint:* If you do not see the Prt Claim selection, refer back to the Troubleshooting box in Module 9.)

Task 6 Note: Manual or Electronic (EDI) Charge Posting

This task may be performed using manual charge posting (instructions given in Module 9, Task 9-1) or using the EDI Interface (instructions given in Module 9, Task 9-5).

In order to use the EDI Interface, your instructor must complete a superbill on the EHR side of the program. This simulates the documentation that a provider would complete. Step-by-step instructions are given in the instructor material on the Online Companion.

Otherwise, manual posting should be used to complete this exercise.

Task 7: Scheduling a Follow-up Appointment

The provider would like to see the patient again in 2 weeks. Schedule an appointment for Wednesday, October 29, 2008, at 10:00 a.m.

Installation Instructions for e-Medsys® Educational Edition

1. Open Internet Explorer and enter www.trimedtech.com/delmar in the address bar.
2. Click the button: Download e-Medsys® to start downloading the e-Medsys® client application.
3. A window will pop-up asking "Do you want to run or save this file?" Click Run.
4. After e-MedsysPM.exe is downloaded, it will ask "Are you sure you want to run this software?" Click Run.
5. The e-Medsys® Educational Edition Setup Wizard will appear. Click Next.
6. Specify the location of the e-Medsys® directory (c:\e-Medsys). Click Next.
7. On the Ready to Install screen, click Install.
8. Type your Enterprise Number (printed on the inside cover of your book) and click OK.
9. Click Yes through the prompt confusing your Enterprise Number.
10. Click Finish to complete the e-Medsys® Setup Wizard.
11. Follow the directions on Page 1 for using the Configuration tool and Logging In to the program.
12. **Please note:** When you are using the e-Medsys® program, a DOS Window will always be present and minimized on your taskbar. Please do not close that DOS Window or you will close the program.

UNINSTALLING e-Medsys®

Vista

1. Click Start > Control Panel then click Programs and Features.
2. Scroll to and click TriMed Technologies e-Medsys® Client for Delmar, Cengage Learning.
3. Click Uninstall at the top.

Windows XP

1. Click Start > Control Panel then click Add or Remove Programs.

2. Scroll to and click TriMed Technologies e-Medsys® Client for Delmar, Cengage Learning.

3. Click Remove.

SYSTEM REQUIREMENTS FOR e-Medsys® EDUCATIONAL EDITION

Minimum Requirements

- Intel Pentium 4 2.0 GHz, 1 GB of available local disk space
- 512 MB memory RAM with Microsoft Windows XP Professional or 1 GB memory RAM Vista Business
- Microsoft Internet Explorer 6 or 7; Internet Explorer 8 running in compatibility mode
- Microsoft Word 2003 or 2007
- Acrobat Reader
- 1024 x 768 x 24 bit display

Third-Party Software

Third-party software (such as Yahoo! and Google toolbars, or Norton and McAfee, etc.) does not follow the rules setup in Internet options; therefore it tends to block e-Medsys® EHR functionality with respect to Pop-ups. If this does happen, then you need to add http://ehr.elearning.emedsys.trimedtech.com to the allowed or safe sites lists of those programs. Follow the instructions in the next section, Internet Settings (Add as Safe Site).

Internet Settings (Add as Safe Site)

1. Open Internet Explorer and go to the Tools menu bar. Select Pop-up Blocker and set to Turn off Pop-up Blocker.

2. Go to Tools and select Internet Options.

3. Select the second tab Security select Trusted Sites and click on the Sites button.

4. Keep the "Require server verification (https:) for all sites in this zone" checked.

5. Add URL as a trusted site (**http://ehr.elearning.emedsys.trimedtech.com**), then click Close.

6. While in the Trusted sites location click on Custom Level. Select Reset To: and select the Low setting and then hit the Reset button. A message will pop-up asking "Are you sure you want to change the settings for this zone?" Click Yes. Then click the Ok button and then click Ok once more to close out of Internet Options.

Installation Location

It is recommended that you install e-Medsys® PM in "C:\e-Medsys®." The regular installation routine will automatically designate this installation location.

Bandwidth Recommendations

It is recommended that you have a minimum Internet bandwidth of 384 kbps for upload and download. If there are multiple workstations utilizing e-Medsys®, then each will require a minimum of 64 kbps of bandwidth per active workstation.

Recommended Screen Resolution

The recommended screen resolution is 1024 × 768 or higher.

Supported Browser

e-Medsys® EHR does not support browsers other than Internet Explorer 6 and 7 (or Internet Explorer 8 running in compatibility mode). Mozilla Firefox and Netscape are not supported.